GRADE 5

Benchmark Assessment

Macmillan/McGraw-Hill

A

The McGraw·Hill Companies

 Macmillan/McGraw-Hill

Published by Macmillan/McGraw-Hill, of McGraw-Hill Education, a division of The McGraw-Hill Companies, Inc.,
Two Penn Plaza, New York, New York l0l2l.

Printed in the United States of America

2 3 4 5 6 7 8 9 RHR l3 l2 ll l0

Contents

Introduction to the Benchmark Assessments

The Benchmark Assessments in this book are designed to measure how well students acquire the Reading and Language Arts knowledge and skills assessed on standardized tests and to provide you with information about which students may benefit from further instruction in a particular topic area.

Each Benchmark Assessment is formatted to familiarize students with the types of passages and items they may encounter on standardized tests. There are two Reading tests, two Revising and Editing tests, and two Written Composition tests included in this book.

Each Reading test includes:

- 42 multiple-choice items similar to those that students may encounter on standardized reading tests.

Each Revising and Editing test includes:

- 32 multiple-choice items similar to those that students may encounter on standardized revising and editing tests.

Each Written Composition test includes:

- A writing prompt, prewriting pages, and an answer document on which students may draft their composition.

How to Use the Benchmark Assessments

The Benchmark Assessments can be used to measure student progress throughout the year. They can be used to measure a student's knowledge of the general domains of reading and language arts independent of the *Treasures* reading program. There are two parallel forms of the test covering the same skills, and they are of equal difficulty. Administer Form A at the beginning of the year and at the end of the year. Administer Form B in the middle of the year.

Sample Questions are included in each Revising and Editing test for students to practice test items. These pages will help students prepare for this assessment, as well as for standardized tests, as they are similar to items that students will encounter on these tests.

The instructional design of the *Treasures* program reinforces the knowledge and skills assessed on these Benchmark Assessments.

Using the Results to Inform Instruction

The scores on the Benchmark Assessments should improve over time. The first Benchmark Assessment is administered in the fall, and scores are likely to be low as the items represent skills that may not have been taught yet. Scores on the assessment administered mid-year should show an increase, and the scores at the end of the year should be the highest. If you compare or graph the results, scores should show an increase for each student. Students who do not show an improvement in scores should be further evaluated for additional support.

Administering the Benchmark Assessments

The Benchmark Assessments will help you identify the skills for which your students may need more instruction and additional practice.

The tests are untimed, and students should be given as much time as they need to respond to each test item. You may wish to administer the Reading Test on the first day, followed by the Revising and Editing Test and Written Composition test. For planning purposes, the tests may take approximately two hours to complete.

Testing Procedures

Before the test: Distribute copies of the Benchmark Assessment and Answer Sheet.

General Directions: These directions apply to the Reading and Revising and Editing Benchmark Assessments. Test-specific directions are noted below. Say: *Write your name and the date at the top of your Answer Sheet.* When all students are finished, say: *Open the test to page 2. To answer a question, fill in the circle on your Answer Sheet for the answer you choose. Be sure to choose only one answer for each question and make your marks dark and neat.*

Reading: Say: *This is the Reading Test.* Answer any questions the students may have. Then say: *You may begin.*

Revising and Editing: Say: *This is the Revising and Editing Test. We will now answer the sample questions together. Look at the directions below the words "Revising and Editing Sample." Follow along as I read them aloud: "Read the introduction and the passage that follows. Then read each question and fill in the correct answer." You may now answer the sample questions.* When students have finished, review the correct answers: S-1 is A, S-2 is H. Answer any questions students may have. Then say: *You may begin.*

Written Composition: Distribute copies of the Written Composition test. Say: *Write your name and the date on the cover of your test booklet. In this test, you will write a composition on a topic given to you. Open your test to the writing prompt on page 2. You will see the prompt, three prewriting pages, and two lined pages. Be sure to write your composition on the lined pages. You do not have to fill both pages, but your composition may not be longer than two pages. Read the prompt on page 2. Raise your hand if you need help reading the prompt.* Allow time for the students to read the prompt, providing help only when asked by the student. When students are ready, say: *You may begin.*

Scoring the Benchmark Assessments

Scoring the Reading and Revising and Editing tests

Use the **Scoring Charts** provided on **pages viii–xi** and the **Answer Keys** provided on **pages 120–127** to record the number of correct items for each student. Use the results to identify the skills for which students need additional instruction and practice throughout the year. The **Treasures Teaching/Practice Opportunities** chart on **pages xii-xiii** identifies where instruction for specific tested skills is provided in the Treasures reading program.

You can save the Scoring Charts for each student as you progress through the year. Compare the results recorded across charts to see where progress has been made and determine where a student may still need additional help.

Scoring the Written Composition

Student writing is assessed in five domains: Focus and Coherence, Organization, Development of Ideas, Voice, and Conventions. Each domain is scored holistically. Teachers should use the scoring criteria contained in the **Writing Rubrics** on **pages 128–131** to determine the overall performance level of the student's writing and assign it one of four score points.

Anchor Papers to help you score the written compositions can be found on **pages 132–139.** These student writing samples illustrate the kinds of responses students are likely to write, as well as the most common kinds of errors found in student writing at this grade level.

Student Name _____

Reading Test Form A

Reading Objectives	Total Number of Items	Number Correct	Total
Objective 1: *Basic Understanding*	14	/14	/14
Objective 2: *Literary Elements*	9	/9	/9
Objective 3: *Analysis Using Reading Strategies*	7	/7	/7
Objective 4: *Analysis Using Critical-Thinking Skills*	12	/12	/12
			/42

Benchmark Assessment

Student Name _____

Revising and Editing Test Form A

Writing Objectives	Total Number of Items	Number Correct	Total
Objective 3: *Organization*	5	/5	/5
Objective 4: *Sentence Structure*	9	/9	/9
Objective 5: *Standard Usage/ Word Choice*	9	/9	/9
Objective 6: *Punctuation, Capitalization, Spelling*	9	/9	/9
			/32

Written Composition Form A

Writing Objectives	Total
Objective 1: *Effective Composition*	
Objective 2: *Command of Conventions*	/4

Student Name _____

Reading Test Form B

Reading Objectives	Total Number of Items	Number Correct	Total
Objective 1: *Basic Understanding*	12	/12	/12
Objective 2: *Literary Elements*	11	/11	/11
Objective 3: *Analysis Using Reading Strategies*	9	/9	/9
Objective 4: *Analysis Using Critical-Thinking Skills*	10	/10	/10
			/42

Student Name _____

Revising and Editing Test Form B

Writing Objectives	Total Number of Items	Number Correct	Total
Objective 3: *Organization*	5	/5	/5
Objective 4: *Sentence Structure*	9	/9	/9
Objective 5: *Standard Usage/ Word Choice*	9	/9	/9
Objective 6: *Punctuation, Capitalization, Spelling*	9	/9	/9
			/32

Written Composition Form B

Writing Objectives	Total
Objective 1: *Effective Composition*	/4
Objective 2: *Command of Conventions*	

Treasures Teaching/Practice Opportunities

Teacher's Edition	TFK Magazine TM
Roots and Affixes— **Greek and Latin Affixes:** Unit 1: 74 ; Unit 2: 138, 172; Unit 3: 307D, 319H, 328, 349D, Unit 4: 413D, 437D, 513D; Unit 5: 549D, 589H; Unit 6: 751C–751D **Affixes:** Unit 1: 59D; Unit 2: 179D, 230; Unit 4: 388, 395, 397, 483D; Unit 6: 713D **Greek and Latin Roots:** Unit 1: 71H, 74, 95D, 112, Unit 2: 239D; Unit 4: 449H; Unit 5: 643D; Unit 6: 740, 752 **Root Words:** Unit 1: 80; Unit 2 148; Unit 3: 265, 361; Unit 5: 559, 599, 603, 649; Unit 6: 665	**Roots and Affixes-** **22, 24, 28** **Suffixes:** 32, 34, 38 **Greek and Latin Roots:** 52, 54, 58, 72, 74, 78, 82, 84, 88
Context Clues: Unit 2: 160, 205; Unit 3: 297, 322, 352; Unit 4: 416, Unit 6: 656, 695, 716 **Context Clues/Multiple-Meaning Words:** Unit 4: 519; Unit 6: 734, 759 **Analogies:** Unit 1: S14, 46; Unit 3: 252; 257; 365; 381; Unit 4: 452, 468; Unit 5: 552; 647	**Context Clues:** 62, 64, 68, 142, 144, 148 **Analogies:** 104 **Synonyms:** 108
Idioms: Unit 1: 36, 46, 47, 131; Unit 3: 269, 338; Unit 5: 536, 612, Unit 6: 671	**Idioms:** 12, 14, 17
Dictionary: Unit 1: S13, 42, 131, Unit 4: 486; Unit 5: 585C–585D, 622; Unit 6: 728	
Summarize: Unit 1: 63A–63B; Unit 2: 161A–161B, 171; Unit 4: 417A–417B; Unit 5: 585B, 637B	**Summarize:** 1, 3, 4-5, 6, 7-8, 11, 13, 14-15, 16, 17-18, 21, 23, 24-25, 26, 27-28
Theme: Origin Myths: Unit 2: 177, 245; Unit 3: 315; Unit 4: 435; Unit 5: 615; Unit 6: 751B **Historical Fiction:** Unit 1: 19, 21, 113, 131; Unit 3: 368; Unit 4: 403	
Structural Elements of Poetry: Unit 1: 120, 122, 123; Unit 2: 154-155, 236-237; Unit 5: 574-575, 639; Unit 6: 784	**Structural Elements of Poetry:** 9, 10, 49, 50, 109, 110, 139, 140
Plot: Unit 3: 293; Unit 6: 664, 668, 670, 738	
Character: Unit 1: 53B, 83, 118; Unit 3: 298, 300; Unit 4: 487A–487B; Unit 6: 672, 698, 707B, 734, 772	
Literary Nonfiction: Biographies: Unit 1: 54, 57, 130; Unit 5: 558-559, 566, 567, 570, 631	
Sensory Language: Sensory Details and Imagery: Unit 2: 237; Unit 3: 370, 381; Unit 5: 572; Unit 6: 706, 744 **Figurative Langauge:** Unit 1: 18; Unit 2: 214-215; Unit 3: 287, 322, 370, 381; Unit 4: 458, 493; Unit 5: 606	**Sensory Language: Similes and Metaphors:** 132, 134, 138

Teacher's Edition	TFK Magazine TM
Narrative Point of View: Unit 3: 359, 3: 381; Unit 4: 506; Unit 5: 533, 542; Unit 6: 676	
Author's Purpose: Unit 1: 56; Unit 2: 142; Unit 2: 183A-183B, 224; Unit 4: 518; Unit 5: 615	**Author's Purpose:** 71, 73, 74-75, 76, 77-78
Text Features: Unit 1: 29; Unit 3: 303, 346; Unit 4: 509; Unit 5: 546; Unit 6: 709, 775	**Text Features:** 62, 64, 67
Author's Viewpoint: Unit 2: 183A-183B, 186; Unit 3: 380; Unit 4: 443: Unit 6: 717A-717B, 745B	**Author's Viewpoint/ Perspective:** 141, 143, 144-145, 146, 147-148
Identify Details in Procedural Text: Unit 2: 150, 209, 244, 245; Unit 3: 344; Unit 3: 345; Unit 6: 711, 721C-721D	
Time Lines: Unit 1: 28-29; Unit 5: 544; Unit 5: 546, 638 **Charts:** Unit 1: 67: Unit 2: 146; Unit 6: 683, 721D, 742	**Time Lines:** 2, 4, 7, 22, 24, 27, 52, 54, 57, 69, 70, 149, 150; **Charts:** 19, 20, 82, 84, 87;
Foreshadowing: Unit 1: 37A-37B, 45, 50, 99A-99B; Unit 3: 281A; Unit 4: 460; Unit 6: 662	
Draw Conclusions: Unit 1: 56; Unit 2: 183A-183B, 199, 224; Unit 4: 401, 518; Unit 5: 615	**Draw Conclusions:** 41, 43, 44-45, 46, 47, 48
Fact and Opinion: Unit 2: 195A-195B, 202, 228, 235B, 244; Unit 4: 441A-441B, 477B; Unit 5: 623A-623B	**Fact and Opinion:** 81, 83, 84-85, 86, 87-88
Organizational Patterns- **Cause and Effect:** Unit 2: 221A-221B; Unit 4: 389A-389B; Unit 5: 581A-581B **Compare and Contrast:** Unit 2: 221A-221B; Unit 3: 311A-311B **Classify and Logical Order:** Unit 2: 234; Unit 4: 389A-389B **Sequence:** Unit 2: 139A-139B, 144, 175B; Unit 3: 315B	**Organizational Patterns-** **Compare and Contrast:** 121, 123, 124-125, 126, 127-128, 131, 133, 134-135, 136, 137-138 **Sequence:** 51, 53, 54-55-56, 57-58, 111, 113, 114-115, 116, 117-118
Synthesize/Make Connections: Unit 2: 153, 170, 175, 229, 235, 237; Unit 3: 311A-311B, 314, 315; Unit 4: 402, 403, 406, 407; Unit 5: 641, 648	
Persuasive Techniques: Recognize Exaggerated Statements: Unit 2: 227; Unit 3: 380; Unit 4: 430, 510, 511; Unit 5: 628; Unit 6: 717A-717B, 745B	

Student Name _____

Date _____

Reading Test
Form A

A Brief History of the Camera

1   Today people all around the world use photography and cameras to learn, share, and express things. But a little over 200 years ago, photographs didn't even exist! While now we use digital cameras to snap and share pictures almost instantly, the first cameras could take eight hours to make an image. The story of how cameras were invented and developed is as interesting as images themselves.

2   In 1826, the French inventor Joseph Nicéphore Niépce used a camera obscura (a device similar to the pinhole camera) to capture a still image on a pewter plate coated with chemicals. It took the exposure eight hours to be completed. An exposure is the amount of light needed for an image to develop. You can still see the image it made on the plate today. Niépce's image is the first photograph.

3   At that time, it took too long to take photographs of people. No one wanted to pose for eight hours. Then Louis-Jacques-Mandé Daguerre, a French chemist and painter, developed a new technology called a daguerreotype. A daguerreotype needed only several minutes to take an exposure. Daguerre made his first daguerreotype of the street below his apartment in Paris. The moving pedestrians and carriages on the street are not visible in the image because they did not stay in place the whole time. But a man who was waiting for a shoe shine during the whole exposure was caught in the image. He was the first person to be photographed!

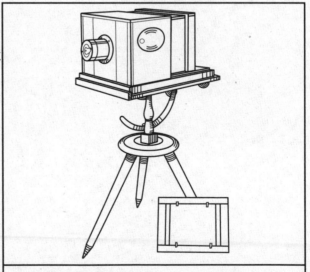
A camera obscura took the first photograph.

© Macmillan/McGraw-Hill

GO ON

4   In the second half of the 19th century, photographic technology advanced rapidly. A man named Felix Tournachon used a balloon high above Paris to take the first aerial photographs, also known as using the bird's-eye view, in 1858. Scottish physicist James Clerk Maxwell used filters to take the first color photograph in 1861—although that technology would not become commonly used for many years. Because of the long exposures, these photographic technologies could capture only still subjects. By 1872, though, people had found ways of capturing movement. The first action photograph was of galloping horses.

5   Before the late 1800s, it was difficult for the average person to try photography. That changed when George Eastman began selling <u>film</u> cameras to the general public in 1888. People could then take personal snapshots as well as studio portraits. Photography became a popular hobby.

A George Eastman camera

6   Today most people use digital cameras, not film cameras. Although digital cameras were being developed as early as the 1980s, true digital cameras were not available to most people until 1990. Today pocket digital cameras have the capabilities to crop and edit images and to print and email photos instantly. It is amazing to consider how the technology has changed since the time of the first image. Imagine what cameras will be like 200 years from now!

A digital camera

GO ON

Page 3

Make a Pinhole Camera

1   Throughout history, humans have been interested in making representations of what they see in the world. The earliest art is probably from around 30,000 years ago, when people used charcoal and chalk to draw animals and other designs on the walls of caves.

2   Ever since then, people have depicted their world using all different types of art, from oil paints and water colors to photographs and video. Drawing or taking pictures are great ways to document and show your world. An interesting way to make art is by using a pinhole camera. You can make a pinhole camera at home using simple household items.

3   **What You Need**
   • a cylindrical box with a lid, such as an oatmeal box
   • a needle
   • black paint
   • black construction paper
   • photographic paper
   • tape

Cave drawings were the first art.

GO ON

Page 4

What to Do

4   Paint the inside of your box with black paint. Paint the lid black on the inside and on the outside. Make the lens by asking an adult to poke a hole on the bottom of your box, using the needle. The smaller the hole the better. Make a shutter by cutting a small piece of black construction paper to cover the hole. Tape the shutter onto the bottom of your box. Tape only the top edge of the shutter.

5   Remove the lid and place a sheet of photographic paper on the inside with the photographic side facing the pinhole. Replace the lid. Be sure to complete this step in the dark to avoid exposing the paper to light too soon.

6   Now, take a picture. Aim the bottom of the can at an object that you find interesting. Take your picture outside where there is plenty of light. Open up the shutter to let the light reflect off your object into your camera. Leave the shutter open for several seconds. Leave the shutter open longer if it is cloudy and shorter if there is lots of sun. An image of the object you pointed your camera at should be appearing on your photographic paper. Then follow the <u>manufacturer's</u> instructions for making the image appear on the photographic paper.

7   Photographs taken with a pinhole camera can be less sharp than photographs taken with a regular camera. You can use this quality for artistic effect. Experiment with your camera to create photographs that depict the world as you see it, and be sure to share your art with other people. Pinhole photography, like all art, is meant to enrich the world and help other people see things in a whole new light.

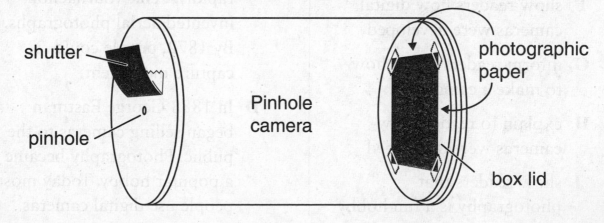

shutter

pinhole

Pinhole camera

photographic paper

box lid

Use "A Brief History of the Camera" (pp. 2–3) to answer questions 1–5.

---

1 The reader can conclude from the information presented by the author that —

   A digital photographic technology has not advanced much in the last 20 years

   B photography has always been a popular hobby

   C photography may become a popular hobby

   D digital photographic technology has advanced a lot in the last 20 years

2 The author probably wrote this article to —

   F show readers how digital cameras were developed

   G inform readers about how to make a camera

   H explain to readers how cameras were developed

   J show readers that photography is a fun hobby

3 Which of these is the best summary of this article?

   A The first camera was created in 1826. Exposures took a long time to be completed. By the late 1800's, cameras were available to everyone and photography became a popular hobby. Today most people use digital cameras.

   B The first camera was created in 1826. A camera obscura was used to capture an image on a plate. The exposure took eight hours to be completed. Today most people use digital cameras.

   C The camera was created in 1826. Technology advanced rapidly. Felix Tournachon invented aerial photographs. By 1872, people could capture movement.

   D In 1888 George Eastman began selling cameras to the public. Photography became a popular hobby. Today most people use digital cameras.

© Macmillan/McGraw-Hill

Page 6

GO ON ➡

4 Look at the chart of information from the article.

Joseph Nicéphore Niépce made the first photograph.

↓

Felix Tournachon used a balloon to take the first aerial photographs.

↓

↓

People use digital cameras.

Which of the following should go in the empty box?

F Louis-Jacques-Mandé Daguerre created a daguerreotype.

G George Eastman began selling film cameras to the general public

H Digital cameras can crop and edit images and print and email photos.

J It took Joseph Nicéphore Niépce's exposure eight hours to be completed.

5 Read the entry below for the word film.

> **film** /film/ *noun* **1.** a motion picture movie **2.** a thin surface covering water **3.** a material used in a camera **4.** a growth in the eye

Which definition best fits the way film is used in paragraph 5?

A Definition 1

B Definition 2

C Definition 3

D Definition 4

Page 7

GO ON

> ### Use "Make a Pinhole Camera" (pp. 4–5) to answer questions 6–10.

6 In making a pinhole camera, what do you do before you make the lens?

  F Tape the shutter onto the bottom of the box.

  G Make a shutter to cover the lens.

  H Paint the lid black on the inside and on the outside.

  J Place a sheet of photographic paper on the inside.

7 In making a pinhole camera, what do you do after you open up the shutter?

  A Replace the lid.

  B Take a picture.

  C Aim at an object that you are interested in.

  D Leave the shutter open for several seconds.

8 The diagram of a pinhole camera helps the reader because it shows —

  F the steps of making a pinhole camera

  G the materials needed to make a pinhole camera

  H what a completed pinhole camera should look like

  J how to make the shutter of a pinhole camera

GO ON →

9 In paragraph 6, what does the word *manufacturer* mean?

A A person or company that makes or creates something

B An image or painting, a representation

C A process of testing or experimenting

D A device used to take photographic images

10 The author probably wrote this article to —

F show readers how to make a pinhole camera

G persuade readers to make a pinhole camera

H inform readers about how a pinhole camera works

J inform readers about the history of pinhole cameras

GO ON

Use "A Brief History of the Camera" and "Make a Pinhole Camera" to answer questions 11–13.

---

11 Look at the diagram of information from both selections.

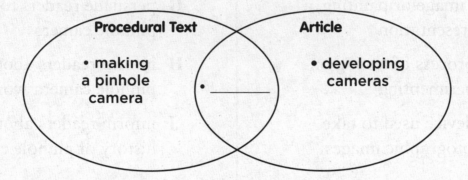

Which description belongs on the blank line?

A How cameras work

B The history of cameras

C The first camera

D The future of cameras

GO ON ▶

12 Which type of camera described in the article is similar to the pinhole camera?

F Daguerreotype

G Camera obscura

H Digital camera

J Film camera

13 One idea presented in both selections is that —

A making a daguerreotype is fun and easy

B making a pinhole camera is fun and easy

C people have always enjoyed taking and sharing photographs of what they see

D people have always created new ways to make images of what they see

GO ON

Page 11

The Littlest Giant

1   When a giant panda is born, it is not so giant. A newborn baby giant panda is no bigger than a stick of butter and weighs only about one quarter of a pound. During its lifetime, this giant panda will grow to be as tall as two or three feet and weigh over 200 pounds. That's around 900 times its size at birth! And all on a vegetarian diet of mostly bamboo!

2   There are only 1,600 giant pandas left in the wild, and more than 150 living in zoos around the world. In the wild, giant pandas live mostly in the mountains of central China. They spend up to 16 hours a day munching on bamboo plants. The rest of the time is spent sleeping or relaxing.

3   An adult giant panda female will mate and have a cub five to eight times in her life. She will spend up to three years taking care of each cub. When a giant panda is born, it is completely helpless. It is tiny and hairless, and its eyes are shut tight, so it cannot see a thing. Some animals, such as horses, are practically born running. They can stand on their own four feet soon after birth and follow their mothers around as they graze. But baby giant pandas are different. A baby giant panda's mother must constantly care for her child for the first few months of its life.

A mother panda and her baby

© Macmillan/McGraw-Hill

Page 12

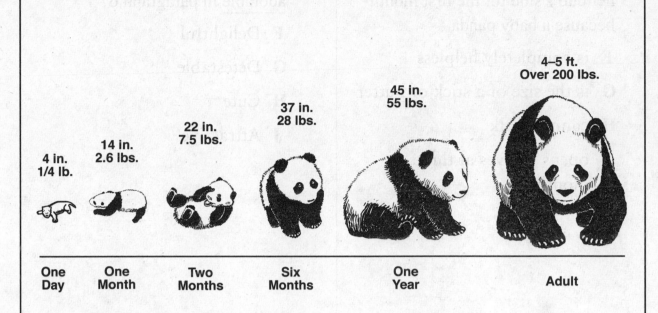

| 4 in. 1/4 lb. | 14 in. 2.6 lbs. | 22 in. 7.5 lbs. | 37 in. 28 lbs. | 45 in. 55 lbs. | 4–5 ft. Over 200 lbs. |
| One Day | One Month | Two Months | Six Months | One Year | Adult |

4   A mother panda has her work cut out for her when she is taking care of a cub. She does not leave the cub's side for even a minute during its first month, not even to eat.

5   After a month, the little cub begins to look more like an adult, and its mother leaves it for very short periods of time to munch on some bamboo. Around this time, the cub opens its eyes and starts to wiggle around. At three months, the cub is much more <u>mobile</u>, and at four months it is very active, crawling on its mother and getting around pretty well on its own. Still, the cub sticks close to its mother during its first year of life. It is not until it is around a year and a half to two years old that the baby giant panda leaves its mother to go off on its own in the wild world.

6   With their black and white fur and fuzzy ears, giant pandas are really quite <u>adorable</u>. It's hard to believe that these gentle giants begin their lives as tiny, helpless babies no bigger than sticks of butter.

GO ON

Page 13

14 A mother panda does not leave her cub's side for the first month because a baby panda —

F is completely helpless

G is the size of a stick of butter

H cannot walk

J opens its eyes at three months

15 In paragraph 5, what does the word <u>mobile</u> mean?

A A hanging sculpture that moves

B Able to move easily

C Able to change quickly

D A motorized vehicle

16 Which word is the opposite of <u>adorable</u> in paragraph 6?

F Delightful

G Detestable

H Cute

J Attractive

17 The author probably wrote this article to —

A inform readers about how pandas live

B explain to readers why pandas live in the wild

C persuade readers that giant pandas are adorable

D inform readers about the growth of baby pandas

© Macmillan/McGraw-Hill

GO ON ➤

18 Look at the chart of information about paragraph 3.

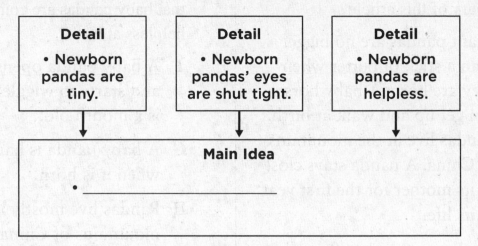

Detail	Detail	Detail
• Newborn pandas are tiny.	• Newborn pandas' eyes are shut tight.	• Newborn pandas are helpless.

Main Idea

• _____

Which statement belongs on the blank line?

F What baby horses can do at birth

G Why baby pandas need constant care

H How many cubs a panda has

J Baby pandas are like baby horses

Page 15

GO ON

19 Which of these is the best summary of this article?

A Giant pandas are no bigger than a stick of butter when they are born. A baby horse can get up and walk at birth. Pandas live in the mountains of China. A panda stays close to its mother for the first year of its life.

B There are only 1,600 pandas left. They live in the mountains of China. At birth, a panda is no bigger than a stick of butter. A panda stays close to its mother for the first year of its life.

C There are only 1,600 pandas left in the world. They live in the wild. Pandas spend up to 16 hours a day munching. They mostly eat bamboo.

D Giant pandas are no bigger than a stick of butter when they are born. A baby panda is completely helpless. A mother panda does not leave her cub for the first month of its life. A panda stays close to its mother for the first year of its life.

20 Which fact supports the idea that baby pandas are completely helpless at birth?

F A baby panda opens its eyes and starts to wiggle when it is a month old.

G A baby panda is hairless when it is born.

H Pandas live mostly in the mountains of China.

J Baby horses can practically walk when they are born.

Page 16

GO ON

21 Which of these statements is an opinion?

   A A newborn panda is no bigger than a stick of butter.

   B There are 1,600 pandas left in the world.

   C Giant pandas are really quite adorable.

   D A month-old cub begins to look like an adult.

22 From the information in the article, how are newborn horses and newborn pandas different?

   F Newborn horses can open their eyes and newborn pandas cannot.

   G Newborn horses stay with their mothers and newborn pandas do not.

   H Newborn horses can walk and newborn pandas cannot.

   J Newborn horses and newborn pandas are hairless.

23 Why was the order of events in this article important?

   A It followed the development of pandas from birth to age two.

   B It followed the development of horses from birth to age two.

   C It showed how baby pandas are different than baby horses.

   D It showed what a baby panda can do when it is one month old.

Page 17

Sports Day

1   The alarm went off: beep beep beep beep. Travis pressed his hand down on the snooze button and rolled over. He was usually a quick riser, but he was not eager to get out of bed today. He had been dreading this day for the entire week. How he wished it were just another Friday . . . any other Friday. Instead, it was the first Friday in June. He laid in his bed, staring up at the ceiling. As the alarm went off again—beep beep beep beep—he inwardly grimaced, and rolled out of bed. He threw on the light athletic wear that he set out the night before; laced up his sneakers; and headed down to breakfast. As he walked down the stairs, he thought about how he never really liked gym class. The thought of a hot June day filled with running around in circles and jumping in place made him want to sit down before he even went outside.

© Macmillan/McGraw-Hill

Page 18

GO ON

2   He stepped into the kitchen and saw that his dad was still home and had not yet gone to work. He was so happy that they would have a chance to talk that he smiled. Then his dad asked him, "So, are you excited about sports day this year, champ?" Travis's smile quickly waned as he didn't answer. Instead, he grabbed his favorite cereal and a bowl. He washed it down with cold OJ. His dad ignored him and droned on, "You've got a beautiful day for it. It's not all that hot today. The high temperature is supposed to be in the low eighties." Travis stopped listening and just rolled his eyes. The last thing he heard as he went out the door was, "Do your best, tiger!"

3   As Travis walked into school, he realized that there was nothing he could do about it. On the first Friday of June, all of the students at Carson Elementary School gathered on the grassy field next to the playground. For everybody else, Sports Day was probably the best day of the school year. For the fifth grade class, Sports Day was extra special. It was the fifth graders' last big school event before they graduated from Carson Elementary. All the kids were gathered with their friends, chatting. Travis could practically feel the energy and excitement coming off his peers. Travis did like one thing. At least he could hang out with his friends for this Sports Day. It would be fun to spend the whole day talking and hanging out. At least, that was the plan.

4   As the day began, he was sitting in the shade on the side of the field talking to his friends, Sam, George, and Erin. As a Sports Day tradition, students were grouped into teams. As Mr. Donogal called out who was on each team, Travis got a bad feeling as he watched his friends go off to their teams. As it turned out, Travis was on the Yellow Team. He couldn't help but wish that he was on the Green Team or the Blue Team. His neighbor, Sam, was on the Green Team. Travis noticed that his other two friends, George and Erin, were on the Blue Team. In fact, he was the only person in his whole class who was on the Yellow Team. Travis noted that the Yellow Team was mainly made up of kids from the other two fifth-grade classes. While his teammates were talking and laughing together, Travis stood off to the side by himself.

Page 19

GO ON ➤

5   Travis kicked his new sneakers in the dirt. He glanced over at the playground, wishing he could skip Sports Day. He thought about how much fun his friends were having without him. Then he thought about how he didn't want to graduate from Carson Elementary. Going to a new school would be just like being on the Yellow Team for Sports Day. He wouldn't know anyone.

6   Then the school principal, Mrs. Trisher, blew a whistle. "Welcome to Sports Day. This is one of the best days of the year because it brings all of our students together. Have a great time and make some new friends today."

7   The first event was the egg race. Students had to balance an egg on a spoon while they walked to an orange cone and back. Then they had to pass the egg and spoon to the next person on their team. The first team to have everyone complete the task, by <u>transporting</u> the egg without breaking it, would win the event. Travis thought that at least it didn't involve running or jumping, and decided he would do the egg race.

© Macmillan/McGraw-Hill

Page 20

GO ON →

8   When it was time for the egg race, everyone but Travis quickly got in line. Travis dragged his feet and ended up at the end of the Yellow Team's line.

9   "On your mark. Get set. Go!" shouted Mrs. Trisher.

10   Students cheered as their teammates carefully balanced their eggs. The Blue Team's egg fell to the ground and splattered right away. The Blue Team was out, but that still left five other teams. There were lots of people on each team, so the races were all close as some people moved really fast with the eggs, and others went very slowly and carefully.

11   When Scott, the student in front of Travis, received the egg, the Yellow Team was in fifth place. Scott raced quickly but carefully, and brought the Yellow Team into third place. He passed the egg to Travis. Travis would have it for the home stretch.

12   "Come on, Travis! We're in third place!" shouted Scott. Travis decided to give it his all. Out of the corner of his eye, he saw that the Orange Team, which had been in first place, had just dropped their egg. Now Travis' team was in second place. "I can do this," he thought. He concentrated on moving as fast as he could without dropping the egg. Before he knew it, he had crossed the finish line. Everyone was celebrating, cheering, jumping up and down, and patting him on the back. Because he put everything he had into it, he had passed the Purple Team without even noticing. The Yellow Team had come in first place!

Page 21

13   Travis set the egg down and took a deep breath. Everyone on the
Yellow Team wanted to give Travis a high-five. As he went down the line
high-fiving everyone, he felt pride because he had really tried his best and
it made the team win.

14   "We're going to have you go last in all the races," said Scott. Suddenly
Travis felt more comfortable.

15   "Maybe the Yellow Team isn't so bad after all," Travis thought.
"And maybe I'll like my new school. I guess I shouldn't have assumed
that I would have a bad day. After all, I've had five other Sports Days,
and they weren't that bad."

16   "Come on, Scott. Let's go over to the bean bag toss," said Travis.

Page 22

GO ON

24 In paragraph 7 what does the word <u>transporting</u> mean?

   F To carry from one place to another

   G To come to the end of something

   H To equalize the weights of two things

   J To spring into the air

25 Which word is the opposite of <u>quickly</u> in paragraph 11?

   A Fast

   B Slowly

   C Rapidly

   D Usually

26 In paragraph 11, when Travis is said to have the egg for the "home stretch," this means —

   F to stretch at home

   G the part at the beginning of something

   H the hardest part of something

   J the part just before the finish line

27 In paragraph 12, what clues helped you know the meaning of <u>celebrating</u>?

   A *Everyone*

   B *on the back*

   C *jumping up and down*

   D *and patting him*

GO ON

Page 23

28 In paragraph 8, when Travis is said to have *dragged his feet*, this means that Travis —

   F pulled his feet over the ground

   G walked slowly on purpose

   H eagerly ran somewhere

   J feet were hurting him

30 The author tells this story from the viewpoint of —

   F Travis

   G the Yellow Team

   H a first-person narrator

   J a third-person narrator

29 How does Scott make Travis feel more comfortable?

   A He passes the egg to Travis.

   B He tells Travis to come to the bean bag toss.

   C He says that Travis will go last in all the races.

   D He brings the Yellow Team into third place.

31 The reader can tell that Travis will cross the finish line because —

   A he decided to give it his all

   B he dragged his feet

   C he felt more comfortable

   D he was passed the egg

Page 24

GO ON

32 Why is paragraph 4 important in this story?

  F The principal's comments help the reader predict that Travis will go to a new school.

  G It shows that Travis does not feel comfortable.

  H The principal's comments help the reader predict that Travis will make new friends.

  J It shows that by giving it his all, Travis succeeds.

33 What happened when the students were grouped into teams?

  A Travis was on the Yellow Team with his friends.

  B Travis was on the Yellow Team without his friends.

  C Travis wished he was on the Yellow Team.

  D Travis wished he was on the Red Team.

34 How does Travis most likely feel at the end of the story?

  F Nervous about Sports Day

  G Disappointed that he is on the Yellow Team

  H More comfortable about going to a new school

  J Excited to be on the Blue Team

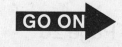

The Open Window

by Edward Rowland Sill

1   My tower was grimly builded,[1]
2   With many a bolt and bar,
3   "And here," I thought, "I will keep my life
4   From the bitter world afar."

5   Dark and chill was the stony floor,
6   Where never a sunbeam lay,
7   And the mold crept up on the dreary wall,
8   With its ghost touch, day by day.
9   One Morn, in my sullen musings[2]

10   A flutter and cry I heard;
11   And close at the rusty casement[3]
12   There clung a frightened bird.
13   Then back I flung the shutter
14   That was never before undone,
15   And I kept till its wings were rested
16   The little weary one.
17   But in through the open window,
18   Which I had forgot to close,
19   There had burst a gush of sunshine

[1]*builded*: an antiquated way of spelling *built*
[2]*sullen musings*: gloomy thoughts
[3]*casement*: part of a window

© Macmillan/McGraw-Hill

GO ON ➡

20   And a summer scent of rose.
21   For all the while I had <u>burrowed</u>
22   There in my dingy⁴ tower,
23   Lo! The birds had sung and the leaves had danced
24   From hour to sunny hour.

25   And such balm⁵ and warmth and beauty
26   Came drifting in since then,
27   That the window still stands open
28   And it shall never be shut again.

⁴*dingy*: dirty and dull
⁵*balm*: mildness, pleasantness

GO ON ➡

Page 27

© Macmillan/McGraw-Hill

35 In line 7 of the poem, what does the word <u>mold</u> mean?

  A A type of fungus that grows on surfaces

  B Give shape to something

  C Influence the quality of or nature of something

  D Fit the contours of something

36 Read the entry below for the word <u>shutter</u>.

> **Shutter** \shə-tər\ *noun*
> **1.** one that shuts **2.** a cover for a window or door **3.** a camera piece that allows light to enter **4.** a piece of a pipe organ

Which definition best fits the meaning of <u>shutter</u> in line 13?

  F Definition 1

  G Definition 2

  H Definition 3

  J Definition 4

GO ON

37 Read the meanings of the word <u>burrowed</u> below. Which meaning best fits the way <u>burrowed</u> is used in line 21?

    A To construct by tunneling

    B A small pack animal

    C A hole in the ground

    D To hide oneself

38 What literary elements does the poet use in this poem to focus on the poem's message?

    F Personification and alliteration

    G Onomatopoeia and rhyme

    H Alliteration and onomatopoeia

    J Alliteration and rhyme

39 How does the alliteration in lines 19 and 20 change the mood of the poem?

    A The lines make the poem darker and weightier than it was before.

    B The lines make the poem lighter and freer than it was before.

    C The alliteration makes an already light poem even brighter and happier.

    D The alliteration does not change the mood of the poem.

Page 29

GO ON

40 The poet's purpose in using the phrase *Dark and chill was the stony floor* in line 5 was to —

F tell the reader what the weather was like

G tell the reader about stone floors

H create an image in the reader's mind

J tell the reader how much he dislikes stone floors

41 What does the phrase "*I will keep my life from the bitter world afar*" in lines 3 and 4 mean?

A I don't like birds or sunshine.

B I will shut myself away from the world.

C I don't like to eat bitter or sour things.

D I will only notice the positive things in the world.

42 The phrase *the window still stands open / And it shall never be shut again* in lines 27 and 28 is important because it tells the reader that —

F the narrator has opened himself up to the world around him

G the narrator likes to have fresh air and won't close the window

H the narrator is going to stay in the tower forever

J the narrator dislikes closed windows

BE SURE YOU HAVE RECORDED ALL OF YOUR ANSWERS ON THE ANSWER SHEET.

Page 30

Student Name _____

Date _____

Revising and Editing Test
Form A

Mc Graw Hill **Macmillan/McGraw-Hill**

Revising and Editing Sample

DIRECTIONS

Read the introduction and the passage that follows. Then read each question and fill in the correct answer.

Anthony wrote this story about his science project. He wants you to help him revise and edit his story. Read the story and think about some changes that Anthony should make. Then answer the questions that follow.

Ready for Lift Off!

(1) Ms. Jillian our science teacher, has assigned us an exciting new project. (2) First, we have to pick a partner to work with. (3) We must choose an interesting topic. (4) We have to choose it from a list by Monday. (5) I will be doing my project with my best friend, Jeremy. (6) We really want to work on a project about space shuttles. (7) We will research our topic at the public library! (8) We also plan on making a model of a space shuttle out of clay and cardboard. (9) Together, Jeremy and I will make our project a success!

S-1 What change, if any, should be made to sentence 1?

A Insert a comma before *our*

B Remove comma after *teacher*

C Change *science* to **sceince**

D Make no change

S-2 What is the **BEST** way to combine sentences 3 and 4?

F By Monday, we must choose a topic and a list.

G We must choose a topic by Monday to put on a list.

H By Monday, we must choose a topic from the list.

J By Monday, we must choose a list from the topic.

Page 2

Joe wrote this report on sharks for his science class. He wants you to help him revise and edit it. Read Joe's report and think about how to fix it. Then answer the questions that follow.

Sharks: A Cool Animal

(1) People think that all sharks are dangerous predators. (2) The reality is that some sharks are dangerous while others are quite harmless. (3) For example, a whale shark is bigger than a bus. (4) However, it only eats tiny fish. (5) "Jaws" is a famous movie about a killer shark.

(6) Sharks are some of the largest fish in the sea. (7) They are very streamlined, which gives them the capabality of moving with great speed. (8) Many sharks can travel more than 20 miles per hour.

(9) A shark has the powerfulest jaw of all animals. (10) Its jaw is also quite unusual. (11) It contains many rows of teeth. (12) When the front row of teeth wears down, it is replaced by the row behind it.

Page 3

© Macmillan/McGraw-Hill

(13) There are many different types of sharks. (14) Blue sharks are among the most common sharks. (15) They are about 13 feet long. (16) They will attack people, but they usually don't get too close to the coastline.

(17) Tiger sharks are extremely dangerous. (18) They are about 10 feet long and have huge mouths. (19) Their curved teeth are as sharp as razors. (20) Tiger sharks will eat anything people have even found old tires in stomachs of tiger sharks.

(21) Hammerhead sharks have large square heads and eyes that are far apart. (22) They may look funny, but hammerhead sharks are excellent hunters. (23) Their able to spot prey as it swims up beside them.

(24) Of course, the great white shark is probably the most famous shark of all. (25) They are the largest predator in the sea. (26) Great white sharks are up to 20 feet long. (27) Great white sharks weigh more than 4,000 pounds.

(28) As you can see, sharks are fascinating creatures.

Benchmark Assessment

1 Which sentence does **NOT** belong in this report?

    A Sentence 5

    B Sentence 8

    C Sentence 14

    D Sentence 22

2 What change, if any, should be made to sentence 2?

    F Change *dangerous* to **dangerus**

    G Add a comma after *dangerous*

    H Change *others* to **other**

    J Make no change

3 What change, if any, should be made to sentence 7?

    A Change *capabality* to **capability**

    B Delete the comma after *streamlined*

    C Change *great* to **greatest**

    D Make no change

4 What change, if any, should be made to sentence 9?

    F Change *has* to **have**

    G Insert a comma after *jaw*

    H Change *powerfulest* to **most powerful**

    J Make no change

Page 5

GO ON

5 Which sentence could **BEST** follow and support sentence 12?

   A People make necklaces from shark's teeth.

   B A shark can grow thousands of teeth in a lifetime.

   C Sharks eat other animals, not plants.

   D Lions and tigers also have powerful jaws and sharp teeth.

6 What is the **BEST** way to revise sentence 20?

   F Tiger sharks will eat anything because people have even found old tires in the stomachs of them.

   G People have even found old tires in their stomachs, so tiger sharks will eat anything.

   H Tiger sharks will eat anything. People have even found old tires in their stomachs.

   J No revision is needed.

GO ON

Page 6

7 What change, if any, should be made to sentence 23?

    A Change *Their* to **They're**

    B Change *swims* to **swim**

    C Change *beside* to **besides**

    D Make no change

8 What is the **BEST** way to revise sentences 26 and 27?

    F Great white sharks are up to 20-feet long and great white sharks weigh 4,000 pounds.

    G Great white sharks are up to 20-feet long and weigh more than 4,000 pounds.

    H Up to 20-feet long, great white sharks weigh more 4,000 pounds.

    J They are up to 20-feet long. They weigh more than 4,000 pounds.

GO ON

Page 7

Naiyma wrote this story about an important event. She would like you to read it and help her revise it. As you read, think about the corrections Naiyma should make. Then answer the questions that follow.

My Paper Route

(1) I was excited when Mr. Dudley at the newspaper office said I could have Danielle's paper route. (2) Danielle had to give it up. (3) Because her family was moving to Texas. (4) We see each other in school sometimes.

(5) When I told my parents the news, they were conserned. (6) They told me it was a big responsibility. (7) After I promised my parents that I was ready for the paper route, my parents they agreed that I could try the paper route.

(8) I began working with Danielle the next week. (9) Unfortunately, she did not seem to think I could handle the job. (10) She acted as if it were a lot of trouble to show me how she rolled and packed the papers.

(11) At the end of the week Danielle she said it was time for me to try the route on my own. (12) I would deliver the newspapers on Sunday morning. (13) I couldn't wait!

(14) On Sunday morning, Danielle helped me fill my bike up with the heavy papers. (15) She watched me wobble down Travis st on my bicycle. (16) When I changed gears, I lost my balance. (17) I fell and spilled papers all over the street. (18) Danielle and I both burst out laughing, and she tells me that the same thing had happened to her.

(19) After my accident, Danielle gave me all the help I needed. (20) During the next few weeks, I improved a great deal. (21) Everyone received their paper right on time! (22) My parents were delighted that I could handle my new job. (23) Danielle was happy that I was taking over her paper route.

9 What revision, if any, is needed for sentences 2 and 3?

   A Danielle had to give it up, her family was moving to Texas.

   B Danielle had to give it up because her family was moving to Texas.

   C Danielle had to give it up because Danielle's family, they were moving to Texas.

   D No revision needed.

10 What change, if any should be made to sentence 5?

   F Delete the comma after *news*

   G Change *were* to **was**

   H Change *conserned* to **concerned**

   J Make no change

11 What is the **BEST** way to revise sentence 7?

   A After I promised my parents that I was ready for the paper route. They agreed that I could try the paper route.

   B After I promised my parents that I was ready for the paper route, they agreed that I could try it.

   C My parents agreed that I could try the paper route after I promised my parents that I was ready for the paper route.

   D No revision is needed.

Page 10

GO ON ➡️

12 What is the **BEST** way to revise sentence 11?

    F At the end of the week, Danielle said it was time for me to try the route on my own.

    G At the end of the week. Danielle she said it was time for me to try the route on my own.

    H At the end of the week, Danielle she said; it was time for me to try the route on my own.

    J No revision is needed.

13 What change, if any, should be made to sentence 15?

    A Change *watched* to **watches**

    B Change *st* to **St.**

    C Change *my* to **mine**

    D Make no change

14 Which sentence does **NOT** belong in the story?

    F Sentence 4

    G Sentence 6

    H Sentence 10

    J Sentence 20

© Macmillan/McGraw-Hill

Page 11

GO ON

15 What change, if any, should be made to sentence 18?

    A Change *I* to **me**

    B Change *happened* to **happening**

    C Change *tells* to **told**

    D Make no change

16 What change, if any, should be made to sentence 21?

    F Change *received* to **recieved**

    G Change *their* to **his or her**

    H Change *right* to **write**

    J Make no change

Page 12

GO ON

Derek wrote this book report. He would like you to read it and help him revise it. As you read, think about ways to improve the report. Then answer the questions that follow.

The World of Robots

(1) If you are interested in robots, then I have a book for you. (2) It is called "The World of Robots" and it was written by Dr. Jerome Gallagher. (3) In the book, Dr. Gallagher describes the amazing things that different robots can do.

(4) Scientists have used robots to explore places where it is hard for humans to go. (5) They used robots, called rovers, on Mars. (6) The rovers explored the surface of Mars. (7) The rovers can move, take photographs collect samples, and do many other jobs. (8) Scientist have also used robots to explore the deepest parts of the ocean.

(9) Some of the most exciting robots have been inspiring by animals. (10) When scientists wanted to create a robot that could move across a sandier area, they studied lizards. (11) Then they built a robot that walks like a lizard. (12) Another robot jumps like a grasshopper. (13) It can leap two feet into the air to avoid obstacles. (14) There are robot fish that swim as good as real fish.

Page 13

GO ON ▶

(15) James McLurkin got the idea for a new type of robot from ants.
(16) He is a scientist. (17) McLurkin always tought ants were interesting.
(18) There are many different types of ants. (19) He liked to watch them
work together. (20) McLurkin decided he wanted to make robots that worked
together like ants. (21) McLurkin calls his groups of robots swarms. (22) The
robots can talk to each other and work as a team. (23) Someday these robot
swarms might be used to explore distant plants. (24) On earth, they might be
used to search for people after an earthquake or other natural disaster.

(25) In the future, robots will be able to do even more amazing things.
(26) Maybe someday everyone will have a robot.

17 What change, if any, should be made to sentence 2?

    A Change *Dr.* to dr

    B Change "The World of Robots" to <u>The World of Robots</u>

    C Change *written* to **writen**

    D Make no change

18 What is the **BEST** way to rewrite sentences 5 and 6?

    F They used robots, called rovers, to explore the surface of Mars.

    G On Mars, they used robots, called rovers, to explore the surface of Mars.

    H Called rovers, they used robots to explore the surface of Mars.

    J To explore the surface of Mars, they used robots that were called rovers.

19 What change, if any, should be made to sentence 9?

    A Change *have been* to **has been**

    B Change *inspiring* to inspired

    C Change *exciting* to **exciteing**

    D Make no change

20 What change, if any, should be made to sentence 10?

    F Change *wanted* to **wants**

    G Change *sandier* to **sandy**

    H Change *studied* to **studyed**

    J Make no change

Page 15

GO ON

21 What change, if any, should be made to sentence 14?

 A Change *are* to **is**

 B Change *real* to **really**

 C Change *good* to **well**

 D Make no change

22 What is the **BEST** way to combine sentences 15 and 16?

 F A scientist James McLurkin got the idea for a new type of robot from ants.

 G James McLurkin, a scientist, got the idea for a new type of robot from ants.

 H James McLurkin got the idea for a new type of robot from ants, who is a scientist.

 J A scientist who is James McLurkin got the idea for a new type of robot from ants.

GO ON

Page 16

23 What change, if any, should be made to sentence 17?

    A Change *interesting* to **most interesting**

    B Change *tought* to **thought**

    C Change *always* to **all ways**

    D Make no change

24 Which sentence does **NOT** belong in the report?

    F Sentence 8

    G Sentence 12

    H Sentence 18

    J Sentence 21

Page 17

GO ON

The advertisement below is a first draft that Jared wrote. The advertisement contains errors. Read the advertisement and think about ways to fix it. Then answer the questions that follow.

The Best New Shoelaces!

(1) For more than 50 years, people in the u.s. have bought their shoelaces from Lovelace Shoelaces (2) Lovelace makes the finest and strongest shoelaces in the country. (3) Now Lovelace offers you a wonderful new shoelace called Perma-Laces. (4) These amazing shoelaces won't never break or wear out. (5) Perma-Laces are made from space-age cotton fiber that can stand up to heat, cold, rain, sleet, and snow. (6) Perma-Laces will last as long as your shoes, if your Perma-Laces don't last as long, we will give you a new pair of laces free!

(7) Jill Austin, a professional basketball player, says, Perma-Laces are the greatest! (8) Tennis star Sam Stevens says, "I will never have to tie my broken shoelaces back together again." (9) International track star and long distence runner Marcus Duffy also praises Perma-Laces. (10) He says, "I have worn through seven pairs of shoes this year I'm still on my first pair of Perma-Laces." (11) Everyone know that broken shoelaces are a terrible problem. (12) Join thousands who have ended their shoelace worries forever. (13) Go out and buy a pair of Perma-Laces today!

Page 18

25 What change, if any, should be made to sentence 1?

   A Change *u.s.* to **U.S.**

   B change *bought* to **bowht**

   C change *their* to **there**

   D Make no change

26 What change, if any, should be made to sentence 4?

   F Change *These* to **Those**

   G Change *wear* to **ware**

   H Change *never* to **ever**

   J Make no change

27 Which sentence would BEST follow and support sentence 5?

   A The shoelaces come in many different colors.

   B No one likes a broken shoelace.

   C You can wear them in any weather conditions.

   D They are made of a space-age fiber.

28 What is the BEST way to revise sentence 6?

   F Perma-Laces will last as long as your shoes. If your Perma-Laces don't last as long. We will give you a new pair of laces free!

   G If your Perma-Laces don't last as long as your shoes, we will give you a new pair of laces for free!

   H Perma-Laces will last as long as your shoes. We will give you a new pair of laces free if your Perma-laces don't last as long as your shoes!

   J No revision is needed.

Page 19

GO ON ➤

29 What change, if any, should be made to sentence 7?

A Change *professional* to **proffesional**

B Insert quotation marks around "Perma-Laces are the greatest!"

C Change *greatest* to **most great**

D Make no change

30 What change, if any, should be made to sentence 9?

F Change *track star* to **Track Star**

G Change *praises* to **praise**

H Change *distence* to **distance**

J Make no change

31 What is the **BEST** way to revise sentence 10?

A He says, "I have worn through seven pairs of shoes this year, I'm still on my first pair of Perma-Laces."

B He says, "I have worn through seven pairs of shoes this year because I'm still on my first pair of Perma-Laces."

C He says, "I have worn through seven pairs of shoes this year, but I'm still on my first pair of Perma-Laces."

D No revision is needed.

32 What change, if any, should be made to sentence 11?

F Change *know* to **knows**

G Change *broken* to **broke**

H Change *terrible* to **terribal**

J Make no change

Page 20

BE SURE YOU HAVE RECORDED ALL OF YOUR ANSWERS ON THE ANSWER SHEET.

STOP

Benchmark Assessment

Grade 5

Student Name _____

Date _____

Written Composition
Form A

McGraw Hill **Macmillan/McGraw-Hill**

Write a composition about a sport or hobby.

The information in the box below will help you remember what to think about when you write your composition.

REMEMBER TO –

❑ write about a sport or hobby

❑ make your composition interesting to the reader

❑ make sure that every sentence you write helps the reader understand your composition

❑ make sure to state your ideas clearly so they are easy for the reader to follow

❑ include enough details to help the reader clearly understand what you are saying

❑ check you composition for correction spelling, capitalization, punctuation, grammar, and sentences

© Macmillan/McGraw-Hill

Page 2

USE THIS PREWRITING PAGE TO
PLAN YOUR COMPOSITION.

© Macmillan/McGraw-Hill

MAKE SURE THAT YOU WRITE YOUR COMPOSITION ON
THE LINES ON PAGES 6–7.

Page 3

USE THIS PREWRITING PAGE TO
PLAN YOUR COMPOSITION.

MAKE SURE THAT YOU WRITE YOUR COMPOSITION ON
THE LINES ON PAGES 6–7.

Student Name _____

USE THIS PREWRITING PAGE TO
PLAN YOUR COMPOSITION.

© Macmillan/McGraw-Hill

MAKE SURE THAT YOU WRITE YOUR COMPOSITION ON
THE LINES ON PAGES 6–7.

Page 5

Answer Document

_____

_____

_____

_____

_____

_____

_____

_____

_____

_____

_____

_____

_____

Answer Document

_____

_____

_____

_____

_____

_____

_____

_____

_____

_____

_____

_____

_____

Page 7

Student Name _____

Date _____

Reading Test
Form B

Macmillan/McGraw-Hill

A Formidable First Lady

Washington, D. C. Burning

1   "The British are coming!" people shouted in panic. The year was 1814 and the War of 1812 was raging. President James Madison begged his wife, Dolley Madison, to leave for safety in Virginia. The British were marching steadily to the White House. "I have things to do first," Dolley said calmly. As the cannons' booming grew louder, Dolley loaded a wagon with Madison's papers, his books, and the White House silver and china. A soldier shouted, "The British are almost at the gate!" But Dolley remained brave. She ran back into the White House and rescued the famous portrait of George Washington. Then she left Washington knowing that she had salvaged all she could. Soon after, the British arrived, grabbing <u>precious</u> treasures from government buildings. Then they burned the White House.

The president's house, 1811

A Popular Partner

2   Before James Madison was President, he was a good friend to Thomas Jefferson. President Jefferson asked him to serve as Secretary of State in 1801, and Madison accepted. This moved James and Dolley Madison into Washington D.C. Dolley became extremely <u>popular</u> for her philanthropic work. She aided in fundraising efforts for the Lewis and Clark exploration and the Louisiana Purchase. She also acted as a hostess for Thomas Jefferson's formal functions. Even before her husband became President, some chroniclers called her the "Presidentress" for her hostess role at the White House.

Dolley Madison

© Macmillan/McGraw-Hill

GO ON

Page 2

3   When Madison ran for the presidency, Dolley helped him every inch of the way. Charles Pinckney, who lost to Madison, said, "I was beaten by Mr. and Mrs. Madison. I might have had a better chance had I faced Mr. Madison alone." Madison became the fourth President of the United States.

The People's House

4   After the British were eventually defeated in the War of 1812, the Madisons returned to Washington. People lined up and cheered Dolley. "We shall rebuild Washington City!" she declared. The rebuilt White House is the same one that you can see if you visit Washington, D.C. today. Dolley decorated it so that visitors would feel welcome. She made it the "People's House" and invited many guests. To make guests feel comfortable, she often walked into a party carrying a book and with her parrot on her shoulder as a joke. When Dolley died in 1849, President Zachary Taylor honored her with the title "First Lady of the Land." This was the first time that the term "First Lady" was used.

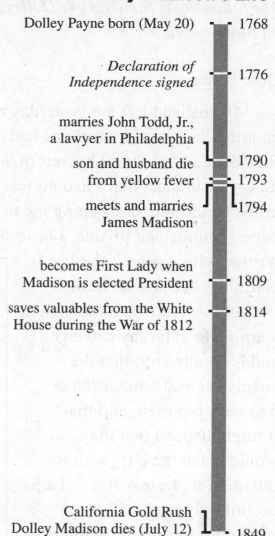

Events in Dolley Madison's Life

Dolley Payne born (May 20) — 1768

Declaration of Independence signed — 1776

marries John Todd, Jr., a lawyer in Philadelphia — 1790
son and husband die from yellow fever — 1793
meets and marries James Madison — 1794

becomes First Lady when Madison is elected President — 1809

saves valuables from the White House during the War of 1812 — 1814

California Gold Rush
Dolley Madison dies (July 12) — 1849

The White House in Washington, D.C.

© Macmillan/McGraw-Hill

Page 3

Letter to her Sister

The following is from a letter Dolley Madison wrote to her sister on August 23rd, 1814.

Dear Sister,

1   My husband left me yesterday morng.[1] to join Gen. Winder. He enquired[2] anxiously whether I had courage, or firmness to remain in the President's house until his return, on the morrow, or succeeding day, and on my assurance that I had no fear but for him and the success of our army, he left me, beseeching me to take care of myself, and of the cabinet papers, public and private. I have since recd.[3] two despatches[4] from him, written with a pencil; the last is alarming, because he desires I should be ready at a moment's warning to enter my carriage and leave the city; that the enemy seemed stronger than had been reported, and that it might happen that they would reach the city, with intention to destroy it. . . . I am accordingly ready; I have pressed as many cabinet papers into trunks as to fill one carriage; our private property must be sacrificed, as it is impossible to procure wagons for its transportation.

The British burning the White House

---

[1] *morng.*: morning;
[2] *enquired*: inquired;

[3] *recd.*: received;
[4] *despatches:* dispatches, or messages;

I am determined not to go myself until I see Mr. Madison safe, and he can accompany me. . . . French John (a faithful domestic[5],) with his usual activity and resolution, offers to spike the cannon[6] at the gate, and to lay a train of powder which would blow up the British, should they enter the house. To the last proposition[7] I positively object, without being able, however, to make him understand why all advantages in war may not be taken.

2   Wednesday morng., twelve o'clock. Since sunrise I have been turning my spy glass[8] in every direction and watching with unwearied anxiety, hoping to discern the approach of my dear husband and his friends; but, alas, I can descry[9] only groups of military wandering in all directions, as if there was a lack of <u>arms</u>, or of spirit to fight for their own firesides!

3   Three O'clock. Will you believe it, my Sister? We have had a battle or skirmish near Bladensburg, and I am still here within sound of the cannon! Mr. Madison comes not; may God protect him! Two messengers covered with dust, come to bid me fly[10]; but I wait for him. . . .

4   Our kind friend, Mr. Carroll, has come to hasten my departure, and is in a very bad humor with me because I insist on waiting until the large picture of Gen. Washington is secured, and it requires to be unscrewed from the wall. This process was found too tedious for these perilous moments; I have ordered the frame to be broken, and the canvass taken out it is done, and the precious portrait placed in the hands of two gentlemen of New York, for safe keeping. And now, dear sister, I must leave this house, or the retreating army will make me a prisoner in it, by filling up the road I am directed to take. When I shall again write you, or where I shall be tomorrow, I cannot tell!!

---

[5]*domestic*: a household servant;
[6]*spike the cannon*: driving a spike through the cannon so that it cannot be used by the British;

[7]*proposition*: proposed plan;
[8]*spy glass*: a small telescope;
[9]*descry*: notice or catch sight of;
[10]*bid me fly*: tell me to leave

Page 5

Use "A Formidable First Lady" (pp. 2–3) to answer questions 1–5.

1 Which word is the opposite of precious in paragraph 1?

  A Cherished

  B Bitter

  C Worthless

  D Dear

2 In paragraph 2, what does the word popular mean?

  F Commonly disliked by people

  G Commonly liked by people

  H Always fun to be with

  J Usually invited to parties

GO ON

Page 6

3 Look at the following summary of information from the article.

Summary

Dolley was married to President James Madison.

_____

Dolley Madison worked to save documents and mementos from
the White House.

_____

_____

Dolley was an inspiring figure at a troubling time.

_____

Which information completes the summary?

A James Madison was a good friend to Thomas Jefferson.

B The United States fought Britain in the War of 1812.

C Dolley used her popularity to support organizations
and help her husband get elected.

D Dolley Madison was the first lady of the United
States of America and did a good job.

GO ON

Page 7

4 What conclusion can the reader draw from the information presented by this author?

- **F** Dolley Madison was a formidable woman who went out of her way to support the American people in a time of great strife.

- **G** Dolley Madison was a good wife and mother.

- **H** Dolley Madison liked James Madison better than Thomas Jefferson.

- **J** Dolley Madison did not want any of the things in the White House to be burned, so she made sure everything was safe from the British.

5 Why was the order of events in the article important?

- **A** The article's order is important because it starts with the War of 1812.

- **B** The article begins at the beginning of Dolley Madison's life and ends with her death.

- **C** The article tells the story of Dolley Madison's life backward, beginning with the end and ending with the beginning.

- **D** The article begins with the British invading and ends by describing the events that follow that event.

GO ON

Page 8

Use "Letter to her Sister" (pp. 4–5) to answer questions 6–10.

6 The author probably wrote the letter to —

   F inform her sister about the events prior to when she fled the White House

   G persuade her sister to leave the White House before the British arrived

   H explain to her sister why they were fighting against the British

   J question whether she should save the cabinet papers

7 In paragraph 2 of this letter, what does the word <u>arms</u> mean?

   A Weapons or ammunitions

   B Limbs on the human body

   C Branches of an organization

   D Equip or prepare for action

8 Which of the following would be helpful in finding information about the meaning of "bid me fly" in paragraph 3?

   F The title of the letter

   G Footnote 10

   H The salutation

   J The closing of the letter

© Macmillan/McGraw-Hill

Page 9

GO ON ▶

9 The author's position on laying explosive powder for the British was that —

   A there was not enough time to do that

   B it was a good way to protect herself and the house

   C it was not the right thing to do

   D it was the right thing to do

10 In paragraph 4, the author states "When I shall again write you, or where I shall be tomorrow, I cannot tell!!" to help the reader understand that —

   F tomorrow she will be able to write another letter

   G she is excited about leaving the White House

   H she knows where she is going next but is unable to tell

   J the situation she is in is uncertain and dangerous

GO ON

> ## Use "A Formidable First Lady" and "Letter to her Sister" to answer questions 11–13.

11 Look at the diagram of information from both selections.

Ideas About Dolley Madison

Biography
- Popular for philanthropic work

• _____

Letter
- Wanted to wait at the White House for the President

Which information belongs on the blank line?

A Dolley Madison was once called the "Presidentress."

B Dolley Madison made people feel welcome and was popular.

C Dolley Madison didn't believe in planning violent attacks on the British.

D Dolley Madison was a brave woman who saved part of her country's history.

Page 11

GO ON

12 Why was the portrait of George Washington mentioned in both the article and the letter?

   F Dolley's rescue of the portrait was an important historical event and the letter shows it was important to her.

   G George Washington was the first president of the United States.

   H Dolley wrote the letter to explain what the portrait was to her sister.

   J The British were coming to burn the White House, and Dolley's letter explains that she wanted to save the portrait.

13 How does the time line help the reader understand when the events Dolley Madison wrote about in her letter took place?

   A It shows that the events in the letter took place before Dolley became the first lady.

   B It shows that the letter was written in 1814, before the White House was rebuilt.

   C It shows that the events took place before the War of 1812.

   D It shows that the events took place after the White House was rebuilt.

© Macmillan/McGraw-Hill

GO ON

Page 12

Sister Sun and Brother Moon

based on a Native American legend

1   A long, long time ago, before people roamed Earth, the Sun and the Moon lived inside the huge, hollow rocks of the great Rock House high on the hilltop. The Rock House was built of solid stone.

2   Sister Sun did not shine in the daytime sky as she does now. Brother Moon did not light up the night sky. Their light was just as bright as we know it today, but it was trapped inside the Rock House. What's more, Sister Sun and Brother Moon never left the house. The only way in or out of their house was to crawl out from underground

3   During this time, all the animals lived in a <u>vast</u> darkness. They did not know day and night. Still, the animals could smell a skunk in their midst. They could hear crickets chirping in the bush. They could taste the cool water from the stream. The animals survived just fine.

4   Coyote was one of those animals who lived in darkness. He could often feel a flea crawling in his fur, and he couldn't stand how it tickled him. He always plucked the little flea off and flicked it into the darkness

5   Now, Coyote was a real trickster. One day, those pesky fleas gave him an idea. Wouldn't it be fun to dump some fleas on Sister Sun and Brother Moon? Instead of flicking the fleas into the air, Coyote began gathering them in a cloth sack. One by one, the sack grew fat with jumping fleas.

Page 13

GO ON ➤

6   One day, Gopher was stumbling along when he bumped into Coyote. He brushed against the cloth sack. He could feel the fleas jumping inside of it

7   "I beg your pardon," said Gopher. "I must be more careful. Say, what do you have in your bag?" Gopher asked. Coyote told him all about his plan to dump the fleas on Sister Sun and Brother Moon

8   "I'm just not sure how to get the fleas inside the Rock House," said Coyote. "It is built of solid stone."

9   "Leave that up to me," laughed Gopher. "I will dig a tunnel all the way to the underside of the Rock House. Then I will crawl back out and you'll dump the fleas into the hole. They will jump the rest of their way into Sister Sun and Brother Moon's home."

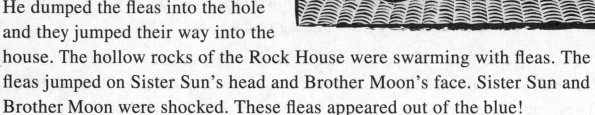

10   Coyote and Gopher snickered all the way to the great Rock House, clutching the bag of bouncing fleas. Once there, Gopher started digging his hole.

11   When the tunnel was finished, Coyote loosened his <u>grip</u> on the bag. He dumped the fleas into the hole and they jumped their way into the house. The hollow rocks of the Rock House were swarming with fleas. The fleas jumped on Sister Sun's head and Brother Moon's face. Sister Sun and Brother Moon were shocked. These fleas appeared out of the blue!

12   Brother Moon scratched so hard at the fleas that he developed sores. In fact, you can still see the scars today on his surface. Sister Sun could not stand the jumping fleas or their sharp and stinging bites. She gathered all her strength and burst out of the Rock House, blasting a hole in the side of a giant rock. Then Brother Moon fled through the hole Sister Sun had made.

13   To this day, the Sun and the Moon circle Earth trying to chase away those fleas. They race inside and outside of their Rock House, one after the other. This is how they share their light with us today.

Page 14

14 Which word is the same as <u>vast</u> in paragraph 3?

    F Immense

    G Weak

    H Medium

    J Diminutive

15 In paragraph 11, when the fleas are said to have appeared "out of the blue," this means that they —

    A came out from a blue spot

    B landed from the sky

    C came as if from nowhere

    D came from a puddle

16 Read the entry below for the word <u>grip</u>.

> **grip** \grip\ *noun*
> **1.** competence in handling a situation **2.** an intellectual hold **3.** a strong hold on something **4.** a small bag

Which definition best fits the meaning of <u>grip</u> in paragraph 11?

    F Definition 1

    G Definition 2

    H Definition 3

    J Definition 4

Page 15

GO ON ➡

17 This legend was probably told to explain —

    A how the sun and the moon became brother and sister

    B why the sun and the moon are never together

    C why the sun and the moon are always moving

    D why coyotes howl at the full moon

18 When Gopher heard Coyote's plan he —

    F offered to help Coyote

    G bumped into Coyote

    H felt the fleas jumping in the sack

    J started digging a hole

19 What event helps the reader predict what will happen next?

    A All the animals lived in darkness

    B Gopher was stumbling when he bumped into Coyote

    C Coyote began collecting fleas in his sack

    D The rocks of the Rock House were swarming with fleas

20 What can the reader tell about Coyote from the legend?

    F He does not like to bother people

    G He does not like Sister Sun or Brother Moon

    H He likes to play tricks on others

    J He does not like being in the darkness

GO ON

Page 16

21 The legend is told from the viewpoint of —

  A a third-person narrator

  B a first-person narrator

  C the coyote

  D the gopher

22 The author's purpose in using the words "sharp and stinging" was to tell the reader —

  F what the fleas do to Sister Sun

  G how the fleas' bites feel to Sister Sun

  H why the fleas bite Sister Sun

  J what the fleas do to Brother Moon

Page 17

GO ON

Calories and Exercise: Pay Attention to Both!

1   Maybe you've seen the nutrition label on a box of cereal and wondered, "Why would I want to know how many calories are in a bowl?" Maybe you've seen your mom or dad using a pedometer. Why are calories and <u>exercise</u> so important? The short answer is that both are essential to your health. If you exercise and pay attention to calories, you will never get sick!

What Are Calories?

2   <u>Calories</u> measure how much energy food provides for your body. One calorie equals the amount of energy needed to heat one kilogram of water one degree Celsius. Although all calories are equal, some foods have more calories than others. If you add up the calories in all the foods you eat, you can determine how much energy you take in during that meal. Calories also measure the energy you use. Your body burns calories all day to get energy. Even when you are resting, your body is using calories!

Calorie Needs

3   Just how many calories does your body need each day? From age 7 to age 10, you require about 2,000 calories every day. You burn most of these calories without even knowing it when you walk, breathe, clean your room, and digest food. You can burn even more calories when you exercise. All people do not burn calories at the same rate. The number of calories a person burns depends on different factors, such as

Your body uses calories to jump

the amount of physical activity he or she does, his or her height, and his or her weight. Some athletes need to eat thousands more calories each day to offset their exercise. They get them by eating nutritious foods.

Storing Calories

4   Some days you may take in more calories than you use. Where does that excess energy go? Your body stores it in muscles and in fat. This is often how people gain weight. For every 3,500 stored calories, a person gains one pound. Other days, you may take in fewer calories than you burn. Where does your body get the extra energy it needs? It takes energy back from your fat and muscles. This is one way people lose weight.

Developing Healthy Eating Habits

5   To stay healthy and fit, you need to pay attention to the foods you eat. It is generally not healthy to eat certain high-calorie foods all the time. A balanced diet is the key to good health. The chart below shows how many calories are in some different foods:

Food	Serving Size	Calories
Ice Cream	1 cup	300
Spinach	1 cup	7
French Fries	1 medium order	430
Orange	1 orange	45
Chicken sandwich	1 sandwich	300

You can see from the chart that because spinach and oranges are low in calories, you can eat a lot of them! Vegetables and fruits also taste great. It's best to talk to an adult like your mom, dad, or a doctor to get an idea of how many calories are healthy for you to eat each day. Make sure that you do not eat too many or too few!

© Macmillan/McGraw-Hill

Page 19

GO ON ➤

The Benefits of Exercise

6   If people regularly eat much more than they need, they can gain weight or develop health problems. Exercising is a good way to balance calorie consumption and good health. Exercise also helps strengthen the heart and muscles and improves flexibility. Best of all, exercise makes people feel good! Studies have shown that when people exercise, they decrease the amount of stress they feel and increase positive feelings. If you play sports on a team or run with a friend, exercise can also be a great <u>social</u> activity.

Follow an Exercise Plan

7   Create an exercise plan for yourself:

Family fun can be healthy, too.

1. Choose some exercises you enjoy. Make sure your parent or a doctor says that those activities are okay.

2. Exercise three times per week.

3. At the beginning of each exercise session, stretch gently to warm up.

4. Spend 30 minutes exercising.

5. End your exercise session with a few minutes of stretching to cool down. You will love exercising!

Calories and Exercise for Fitness and Fun

8   Paying attention to calories and exercise isn't just important: it's also fun. You can have fun experimenting in the kitchen with healthy recipes and new ingredients. Exercise is a great way to get in a good mood and socialize. So read the nutrition label on your granola bar, lace up your sneakers, stay healthy, and have fun!

GO ON

Page 20

23 Read the entry below for the word exercise.

> **exercise** \ek′ sər,sīz\ *noun*
> **1.** the employment of action
> **2.** a problem ot task one does to master a skill **3.** exertion for the sake of physical fitness and health **4.** a ceremony or exhibit in public

Which definition best fits the meaning of exercise in paragraph 1?

A Definition 1

B Definition 2

C Definition 3

D Definition 4

24 In paragraph 2 of this article, what does the word calories mean?

F The amount of food you should eat each day

G The energy needed to heat one kilogram of water one degree Celsius

H The energy needed to cool one kilogram of water one degree Celsius

J The amount of energy you burn by exercising

25 In paragraph 6 of this article, what clues help you know the meaning of social?

A *team, friend*

B *play, run*

C *exercise, sports*

D *great, also*

GO ON

26 The author's position on consuming calories is that you should —

    F consume high-calorie foods whenever possible

    G consume low-calories foods whenever possible

    H be aware of calories and never eat too many or too few

    J eat thousands more calories each day to offset your exercise

27 Which statement seems to be an exaggeration of the facts in this article?

    A Do not eat too many or too few calories.

    B Athletes need to eat more calories each day to offset their exercise.

    C You will never get sick if you exercise and pay attention to calories.

    D You can have fun experimenting with healthy recipes in the kitchen.

28 What conclusion can be drawn from the information in the chart in paragraph 5?

    F All foods have the same number of calories.

    G All foods have the same serving size.

    H Different foods contain different amounts of calories.

    J Spinach has more calories than ice cream.

29 When making an exercise plan, what is the first step to follow?

    A Stretch to warm up at the beginning of your exercise session.

    B End your activity with a cool down and stretching.

    C Exercise at least three times each week.

    D Choose an activity and check with your parent or a doctor to make sure it is okay.

© Macmillan/McGraw-Hill

GO ON

Page 22

30 The author probably wrote the article to —

   F inform readers about the dangers of high-calorie foods

   G persuade the reader to pay attention to calories and exercise

   H explain to the reader how athletes get enough calories

   J question whether readers knew what calories are

31 What information in this article is presented as a fact?

   A All people do not burn calories at the same rate.

   B You will love exercising.

   C Your parents might use a pedometer.

   D Vegetables and fruits taste great.

32 Why is the order of ideas in paragraph 7 so important?

   F The order shows how activities are alike and different.

   G The order shows the sequence for developing an exercise plan.

   H The order shows the effect of starting an exercise plan.

   J The order shows what type of exercise plan to develop.

Page 23

GO ON

The Unsinkable Fortunes

Setting:

Onboard the Titanic, near Newfoundland. Constructed in the early 1900s, the Titanic was one of the largest ships ever built. The makers of the ship were so confident in this design that they called it unsinkable. The Titanic's first voyage began on April 10, 1912. On the night of April 14th, while sailing through icy waters, the ship struck an iceberg.

Characters:

Molly Fortune: a 10-year-old girl who is heading back to her home in New York from a family trip to Europe

Lily Fortune: Molly's 7-year-old sister

Archie Fortune: Molly's 13-year-old brother

Betsey Fortune: Molly's 15 year-old sister

Mother: Molly's mother

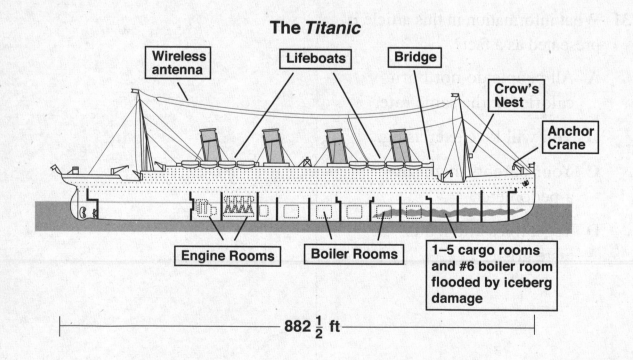

The *Titanic*

Wireless antenna

Lifeboats

Bridge

Crow's Nest

Anchor Crane

Engine Rooms

Boiler Rooms

1–5 cargo rooms and #6 boiler room flooded by iceberg damage

882 ½ ft

Page 24

© Macmillan/McGraw-Hill

Scene I:

A dark cabin aboard the Titanic. It is just before midnight, and Molly, Lily, and Mother are fast asleep in their beds. Suddenly, there is a loud BOOM! and they all jerk awake.

LILY: Momma! What was that?

ARCHIE: What's going on? Is someone at the door?

MOTHER: Shh, it's all right, children. It was just some noise. I wonder where Betsey and Molly are off to?

ARCHIE: They went up to see the stars. I came back because it is such a cold night. But Molly wanted Betsey to take her to hear the band.

LILY: So long as they don't go to the pool without me. I still can't believe that our ship has a pool! The Titanic really is a floating palace —

The door bursts open and Molly and Betsey come rushing in.

MOLLY: Iceberg! We've hit an iceberg!

ARCHIE: It's no matter. Everyone knows that this ship is unsinkable!

LILY: But anything can sink! Momma, I'm afraid.

MOTHER: I don't hear anyone else about in the halls. If something is amiss, they will send for us.

ARCHIE: This ship has the best technology man has made. I read all about it. It's truly unsinkable!

BETSEY: Mama, perhaps we should go upstairs and see what is happening.

MOTHER: Oh, I wish your father was with us! He would know what to do.

LILY: I miss papa.

MOLLY: We all do. But we'll see him in New York soon.

MOTHER: I think you are right, Betsey. Let's all go up and see what we can find out. Put on your coats and boots.

Page 25

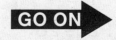

LILY: I'm scared. What if the ship's not as strong as we think?

MOLLY (*giving Lily a hug*): It will be fine, Lily.

MOTHER: Oh, Archie, can you check that trunk for our travel documents? They almost slipped my mind. Let's go quickly!

The family leaves the room.

Scene II:
Mother, Archie, Molly, and Lily are huddled on the top deck. There aren't many people around them, but crew members keep running by.

MOTHER: Where are Archie and Betsey? I wonder if they have found anyone to speak with?

MOLLY: The crew seems troubled. They are running around like mad!

MOTHER: It seems like something is wrong, after all. Look, those men are readying the lifeboats!

LILY: Do you think we'll have to leave the ship on them?

MOLLY: I don't think they've issued a warning for the passengers yet. I heard a crew member telling another that it was time to start waking passengers, though.

Page 26

Betsey and Archie return. They are holding five life vests.

MOTHER: Life vests! We were right to be concerned!

MOLLY: But this ship is unsinkable! I just can't believe it!

BETSEY: We have to put these on and board a lifeboat. I'm afraid we've hit an iceberg and the ship tore badly.

ARCHIE: Water has been flooding the lowest levels for an hour. It looks like the "unsinkable" ship could sink!

Everyone gasps and reacts with amazement and fear.

MOTHER: Thank goodness we came above deck and are prepared. Imagine if we had slept through this all.

BETSEY: They've already radioed for help, and they are setting off fireworks to warn other ships. A ship from New York is headed our way, the Carpathia. We will be able to take her home.

ARCHIE: The crew will help all the other passengers <u>evacuate</u> the ship, but they need us to start the process by getting to safety. We need to get on a lifeboat and leave the ship.

MOLLY: How lucky we were to be up here looking at the stars when it happened.

MOTHER: We are lucky. Let's hurry and get on board the lifeboat. Perhaps this ship is not unsinkable after all, but our family sure is.

The family helps each other board a lifeboat. The lights dim as they settle down into it, holding hands.

Epilogue: There were not enough lifeboats on board for all of the passengers. Hours after the Titanic sank, another boat came close enough to rescue 705 survivors. But 1,522 people were lost at sea.

Page 27

GO ON

33 In Scene I, when Mother says that something "slipped my mind," this means to —

A fall on something

B remember something

C forget something

D want something

34 In Scene II, when Archie tells everyone that they need to "get on the lifeboat," what clues help the reader know the meaning of the word <u>evacuate</u>?

F *crew* and *help*

G *passengers* and *need*

H *safety* and *leave*

J *start* and *getting*

35 The author probably wants the reader to understand —

A why the Titanic sank

B who all of the passengers on the Titanic were

C what is was like to be a passenger on the Titanic

D how the Titanic hit an iceberg

36 Why was it fortunate that Molly and Betsey were on deck when the accident occurred?

F They got to enjoy looking at the stars.

G Otherwise they all might still be asleep in their room.

H Molly got to see the band play.

J Lilly would have been scared if she had seen the accident.

GO ON

Page 28

37 What happened when Betsey said that they should go upstairs?

   A Everyone got worried about getting on a lifeboat.

   B Mother agreed and they all went to the top deck.

   C Lily got upset and wanted to stay in the room.

   D Molly wanted to see the band play.

38 The reader can tell that the Fortunes will survive because they —

   F go to the top deck to see what happened

   G heard a loud noise in their cabin

   H got into the lifeboat

   J brought their travel documents

39 Look at the chart of information from the play.

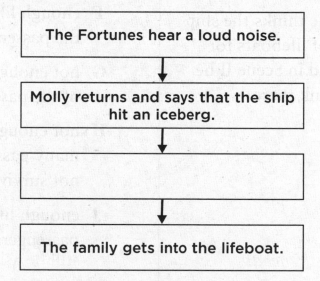

The Fortunes hear a loud noise.

↓

Molly returns and says that the ship hit an iceberg.

↓

↓

The family gets into the lifeboat.

Which of the following should go in the empty box?

   A They are told that water has flooded the ship.

   B They are told to get into the lifeboat.

   C There were not enough lifeboats for all of the passengers.

   D They forget their travel documents.

Page 29

40 How did Archie's feelings about the Titanic change by the end of the play?

  F In Scene I, he thinks the ship might sink and in Scene II he thinks it is unsinkable.

  G In Scene I, he thinks the ship is unsinkable and in Scene II he thinks it might sink.

  H In Scene I, he thinks the ship is the wonder ship and in Scene II he thinks it is unsinkable.

  J In Scene I, he thinks the ship has plenty of lifeboats for everyone and in Scene II he does not think there are enough.

41 What was an important role for Betsey in this play?

  A Betsey comforts Lilly when she is worried.

  B She stays with her mother.

  C Betsey finds out what the family should do.

  D She stays with Molly.

42 The author probably wants the reader to understand that there were —

  F enough lifeboats and all of the passengers survived

  G not enough lifeboats and all of the passengers survived

  H not enough lifeboats and many passengers did not survive

  J enough lifeboats and many passengers did not survive

© Macmillan/McGraw-Hill

Page 30

BE SURE YOU HAVE RECORDED ALL OF YOUR ANSWERS
ON THE ANSWER DOCUMENT.

STOP

Student Name _____

Date _____

Revising and Editing Test
Form B

Macmillan/McGraw-Hill

Anthony wrote this story about his science project. He wants you to help him revise and edit his story. Read the story and think about some changes that Anthony should make. Then answer the questions that follow.

Ready for Lift Off!

(1) Ms. Jillian our science teacher, has assigned us an exciting new project. (2) First, we have to pick a partner to work with. (3) We must choose an interesting topic. (4) We have to choose it from a list by Monday. (5) I will be doing my project with my best friend, Jeremy. (6) We really want to work on a project about space shuttles. (7) We will research our topic at the public library! (8) We also plan on making a modul of a space shuttle out of clay and cardboard. (9) Together, Jeremy and I will make our project a success!

S-1 What change, if any, should be made to sentence 1?

   A Insert a comma before *our*

   B Remove comma after *teacher*

   C Change *science* to **sceince**

   D Make no change

S-2 What is the **BEST** way to combine sentences 3 and 4?

   F By Monday, we must choose a topic and a list.

   G We must choose a topic by Monday to put on a list.

   H By Monday, we must choose a topic from the list.

   J By Monday, we must choose a list from the topic.

© Macmillan/McGraw-Hill

Page 2

The report below is a first draft that Carlos wrote for his teacher. He wants you to help him edit and revise it. Read the report and think about how Carlos can correct and improve it. Then answer the questions that follow.

Amazing Parrots

(1) African gray parrots have been popular pets for centuries. (2) Parrots are famous for being able to talk. (3) They are able to pick up common words and sayings that their owners use. (4) Parrots are also able to copy noises from around the house, such as a doorbell ringing. (5) An owner who spends a lot of time with his or her parrot can teach them to say many things. (6) Parakeets are also popular pets, but they can't copy voices and noises.

Page 3

(7) Some scientists believe African gray parrots are capable of doing much more than copying words and sounds. (8) For many years, dr. Irene Pepperberg has been working with parrots. (9) Her studies show that parrots are very smart animals. (10) In one experiment, Pepperberg hold up different objects and the parrots are able to say what color the object is and what it is made of. (11) Her parrots can also count.

(12) Dr. Pepperberg worked with one parrot for a long time. (13) His name was Alex he was able to do some amazing things. (14) He knew the words for colors, numbers, and many other objects. (15) In one experiment, Alex was shown a collection of objects that included a number of blue blocks, green blocks, and balls. (16) Then he was asked, "How many blue blocks? (17) Alex was able to correctly answer "six." (18) It didn't matter how many other blue things there were or how many other blocks. (19) Alex could tell which objects were both blue and a block. (20) He counted them all!

(21) Dr. Pepperberg and her fellow scientists have done a number of other studies to show how African gray parrots think. (22) She believes that these parrots learn and understand language in the same way children do. (23) While these studies help people learn about parrots, another affect is that they help scientists know more about how humans learn languages.

GO ON

Page 4

1 What change, if any, should be made to sentence 5?

   A Change *who* to **whom**

   B Insert a comma after *parrot*

   C Change *them* to **it**

   D Make no change

2 What change, if any, should be made to sentence 8?

   F Change *For* to **After**

   G Delete the comma after *years*

   H Change *dr.* to **Dr.**

   J Make no change

3 What change, if any, should be made to sentence 10?

   A Change *hold* to **holds**

   B Change *different* to **diffarance**

   C Change *the parrots* to **them**

   D Make no change

4 What is the BEST way to revise sentence 13?

   F Alex was his name and Alex he was able to do some amazing things.

   G His name was Alex, he was able to do some amazing things.

   H While his name was Alex, Alex was able to do some amazing things.

   J His name was Alex and he was able to do some amazing things.

Page 5

GO ON

5 What change, if any, should be made to sentence 16?

   A Change *Then* to **Than**

   B Delete the comma after *asked*

   C Place a quotation mark after the question mark

   D Make no change

6 What is the BEST way to combine sentences 19 and 20?

   F Alex could tell which objects were both blue and a block although he counted them all!

   G Alex could tell which objects were both blue and a block but counted them all!

   H Alex could tell which objects were both blue and a block, and he counted them all!

   J Alex could tell which objects were both blue and a block he counted them all!

Page 6

GO ON

7 What sentence does NOT belong in this report?

   A Sentence 2

   B Sentence 6

   C Sentence 11

   D Sentence 21

8 What change, if any, should be made to sentence 23?

   F Change *studies* to **study's**

   G Change *affect* to **effect**

   H Change *languages* to **langwiches**

   J Make no change

Lauren wrote this story about a special memory. She wants you read her story and help her edit it. As you read, think about ways to improve the story. Then answer the questions that follow.

A Special Memory

(1) Last winter I took a trip that I will never forget. (2) I spent a week at my cousin Emily's house in New York City. (3) I've been to visit my cousin many times before, but this trip was different. (4) It was the first time I spent a week there without my parents.

(5) I have to admit that before the trip I felt real nervous. (6) I didn't know what is was going to be like. (7) I knew I was going to miss my family and friends. (8) I was sad about leaving my dog at home.

(9) I quickly realized that I didn't have anything to worry about, because Emily made me feel right at home! (10) She showed where I was going to sleep and she even made room in her closet for my clothes. (11) There are three hundred apartments in her building.

© Macmillan/McGraw-Hill

GO ON

Page 8

(12) Emily and her family took me somewhere new every day. (13) On the first day, we went to the Museum of Natural History. (14) Its so big that you could spend a week there! (15) My favorite part was the butterfly room. (16) It is filled with butterflies from around the world. (17) The butterflies are colorful. (18) Visitors walk through the room and get to see the butterflies up close. (19) One butterfly even landed on my arm!

(20) We also went to the Empire State Building. (21) It is the tallest building in New York. (22) After waiting in a long line, we ridded the elevator to the top. (23) It was a clear, sunny day and we could see for miles. (24) I took a lot of photografs to show my family.

(25) On my last day, we went ice skating at big rink in the park. (26) It was a little hard to skate. (27) Crowds of people everywhere. (28) We had hot chocolate afterwards to warm up. (29) It was a great way to end the week.

9 What change, if any, should be made to sentence 5?

   A Insert a comma after *trip*

   B Change *real* to really

   C Change *nervous* to nervis

   D Make no change

11 Which sentence does NOT belong in the story?

   A Sentence 5

   B Sentence 11

   C Sentence 21

   D Sentence 28

10 What change, if any, should be made to sentence 9?

   F Change *realized* to **realizing**

   G Delete the comma after *about*

   H Change *right* to **write**

   J Make no change

12 What change, if any, should be made to sentence 14?

   F Change *Its* to It's

   G Change *big* to **bigger**

   H Change *spend* to spent

   J Make no change

GO ON ➡

Page 10

13 What is the best way to combine sentences 16 and 17?

   A The colorful butterflies are from around the world and fill the room.

   B It is filled with butterflies that are colorful and from around the world

   C From around the world, it is filled with colorful butterflies.

   D It is filled with colorful butterflies from around the world.

14 What change, if any, should be made to sentence 22?

   F Delete the comma after *line*

   G Change *ridded* to **rode**

   H Change *elevator* to **elevetor**

   J Make no change

Page 11

GO ON

15 What change, if any, should be made to sentence 24?

   A Change *photografs* to **photographs**

   B Change *show* to **showed**

   C change *my* to **mine**

   D Make no change

16 What is the BEST way to rewrite sentences 26 and 27?

   F It was a little hard to skate because crowds of people they was everywhere.

   G It was a little hard to skate and crowds of people were everywhere.

   H It was a little hard to skate, crowds of people were everywhere.

   J It was a little hard to skate because crowds of people were everywhere.

GO ON ▶

This is a report that Kevin wrote about tornadoes. Kevin would like you to help him edit his report. As you read, think about ways to fix it. Then answer the questions that follow.

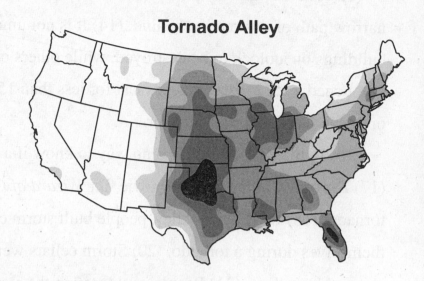

Tornado Alley

Tornado Occurrence per 10,000 square miles

0 0.5 1 3 5 7

Annual Average (1950–1995)

Tornadoes

(1) Tornadoes are one of nature's most destructive storms. (2) They can form in any place and at any time. (3) There is one area in the Midwestern United States that has more tornadoes than anywhere else in the world.

(4) People call this part of the Midwest "Tornado Alley" because there are so many tornadoes there.

(5) Why are tornadoes are common in the Midwestern United States? (6) In the spring and summer, cold, dry air from Canada and warm, moist air from the Gulf of Mexico meet, and severe thunderstorms develop.

(7) A tornado forms when swirling air from inside the storm reaches down and makes contact with the ground. (8) This colum of spinning air can cause a tremendous amount of damage. (9) A tornado's high winds cause most of the damage. (10) Tornadoes knock down houses. (11) Tornadoes uproot trees, and tornadoes also throw cars through the air.

Page 13

GO ON ▶

(12) There is no way predict a tornado's path. (13) It can leave a very narrow path of destruction behind. (14) It is not unusual for some homes and buildings on a block to be destroyed, while others on the same block are left untouched. (15) Most tornadoes last for less than 15 minutes but the worse ones can last for almost an hour.

(16) In the past, people had no way to know if a tornado was coming. (17) Dororthy, in the famous movie *The Wizard of Oz,* was surprised by a tornado. (18) In Tornado Alley, people built storm cellars. (19) To protect themselves during a tornado. (20) Storm cellars were deep holes in the ground covered by a door. (21) People could stay in the storm cellar until the tornado had passed by.

(22) Today meteorologists are better able to predict when tornadoes are possible. (23) The national weather service has a system to keep people informed about severe weather. (24) They issue a tornado watch when the weather conditions are right for a tornado to form and a tornado warning when a tornado has been sighted. (25) These warnings help people better prepare for tornadoes.

GO ON

Benchmark Assessment

17 Which transition word could BEST be added to the beginning of sentence 3?

    A Also

    B Because

    C Therefore

    D However

18 Which change, if any, should be made to sentence 8?

    F Change *colum* to **column**

    G Change *cause* to **causes**

    H Change *amount* to **amounts.**

    J Make no change

19 Which sentence can BEST follow and support sentence 9?

    A The winds can be almost 300 miles per hour.

    B Scientists study tornadoes.

    C Thunderstorms cause damage, too.

    D Tornadoes sometimes form after hurricanes.

20 What is the BEST way to revise sentences 10 and 11?

    F Tornadoes, they knock down houses, and uproot trees. They also throw cars through the air.

    G Tornadoes knock down houses. Uproot trees. Throws cars through the air.

    H Tornadoes knock down houses and tornadoes uproot trees and tornadoes throw cars through the air.

    J Tornadoes knock down houses, uproot trees, and throw cars through the air.

Page 15

GO ON ➡

21 What change, if any, should be made to sentence 15?

   A Change *last* to **lasted**

   B Change *worse* to **worst**

   C Change *almost* to **allmost**

   D Make no change

22 What revision, if any, should be made to sentences 18 and 19?

   F People built storm cellars in Tornado Alley to protect themselves during a tornado in Tornado Alley.

   G In Tornado Alley, people built storm cellars to protect themselves during a tornado.

   H In Tornado Alley, people built storm cellars, protecting themselves during tornado.

   J No revision is needed.

23 What change, if any, should be made to sentence 23?

   A Change *national weather service* to **National Weather Service**

   B Change *has* to **have**

   C Change *informed* to **information**

   D Make no change

24 Which of these sentences does NOT belong in the report?

   F Sentence 7

   G Sentence 14

   H Sentence 17

   J Sentence 22

GO ON

Sherice wrote this story about a camping trip. Read Sherice's story and think about how she should improve it, then answer the questions that follow.

My Camping Trip

(1) Beep, beep, beep. (2) The sound was my alarm. (3) I was not excited to get up. (4) When I went downstairs for breakfast, I saw that my mom, dad, and sister Iris were full of energy.

(5) "Here's your cereal, Alicia," my dad said cheerful.

(6) "Eat up," Mom added, "you'll need energy for hiking."

(7) "Hurry up," Iris said. (8) "Everyone are ready to go."

(9) My parents had planned this hiking trip weeks ago. (10) I wondered how they could be so excited about spending the day hiking up a mountain.

(11) The car ride was pleasant. (12) It was October, so the leaves were had turned beautiful colors. (13) But then we arrived at the mountain.

© Macmillan/McGraw-Hill

(14) "Hop to," Mom said. (15) "We want to make it to the top before sundown!" (16) We found the trail and headed into the woods. (17) It was a very steep trail. (18) I felt tired before we'd gone half a mile. (19) My family was gushing about the leaves and sunlight. (20) I didn't want to intarup their conversation, so I kept my head down and marched on.

(21) Finally, my mom said we could take a break and stop to eat and it seemed like we been walking for days. (22) I sat down and looked up at the leafy ceiling above me. (23) The leaves were pretty, but I still wished I could go home.

(24) "You know, Alicia, these woods are full of mosses and lichens" my dad said.

(25) "What are mosses and lichens?" said Iris.

(26) "Mosses are plants without flowers or roots," said Mom. (27) She pointed to a velvety patch that was covering a boulder. (28) "That's moss."

(29) "Cool. So what's lichen?" I asked.

(30) "Lichens grow on rocks, too," Dad answered, "but they are actually different plants growing all together." (31) He pointed to lichens on a rock. (32) It looked like a tiny, green forest with miniature trees. (33) I was intrigued. (34) I had no idea the forest floor was so interesting! (35) Now, I wanted to look for the mosses and lichens sprouting below me. (36) When we finished hiking, I felt happily to have spent the day discovering nature.

Benchmark Assessment

25 What change, if any, should be made to sentence 5?

   A Change *your* to you're

   B Delete the comma after *Alicia*

   C Change *cheerful* to **cheerfully**

   D Make no change

26 What change, if any, should be made to sentence 8?

   F Change *Everyone* to **Everyone's**

   G Change *are* to **is**

   H Change *go* to **going**

   J Make no change

27 What change, if any, should be made to sentence 20?

   A Change *intarup* to **interrupt**

   B Delete the comma after ***conversation***

   C Change *kept* to **keep**

   D Make no change

28 What is BEST way to combine sentences 17 and 18?

   F Because it was a very steep trail, I felt tired before we'd gone half a mile.

   G While it was a very steep trial, I felt tired before we'd gone half a mile.

   H It was a very steep trail, I felt tried before we gone half a mile.

   J When it was a very steep trail, I felt tried before we'd gone half a mile.

29 What is the BEST way to revise sentence 21?

  A Finally, it seemed like we had been walking for days my mom said we could take a break, stop to eat.

  B Finally, my mom said we could take a break and stop to eat when it seemed like we had been walking for days.

  C Finally, my mom said we could take a break and stop to eat. It seemed like we had been walking for days.

  D No revision is needed.

30 What change, if any, should be made to sentence 24?

  F Change *these* to **them**

  G Insert a comma after *lichens*

  H Change *said* to **saying**

  J Make no change

31 Which sentence can BEST follow and support sentence 26?

  A "They look like green carpets on the rocks."

  B "You can read about them."

  C "You can see moss in the woods."

  D "Moss are not like flowers."

32 What change, if any, should be made to sentence 36?

  F Change *discovering* to **discovered**

  G Changed *finished* to **finushed**

  H Change *happily* to **happy**

  J Make no change

BE SURE YOU HAVE RECORDED ALL OF YOUR ANSWERS ON THE ANSWER SHEET.

Page 20

Student Name _____

Date _____

Written Composition
Form B

McGraw Hill **Macmillan/McGraw-Hill**

Write a composition about
making the school year longer.

The information below will help you remember what you should think about when you write your composition.

REMEMBER TO –

❏ write about a longer school year

❏ make your composition interesting to the reader

❏ make sure that every sentence you write helps the reader understand your composition

❏ make sure to state your ideas clearly so they are easy for the reader to follow

❏ include enough details to help the reader clearly understand what you are saying

❏ check your composition for correct spelling, capitalization, punctuation, grammar, and sentences

© Macmillan/McGraw-Hill

Page 2

Student Name _____

```
┌─────────────────────────────────┐
│   USE THIS PREWRITING PAGE TO    │
│    PLAN YOUR COMPOSITION.        │
└─────────────────────────────────┘
```

Page 3

```
┌──────────────────────────────────────────────┐
│  MAKE SURE THAT YOU WRITE YOUR COMPOSITION     │
│        ON THE LINES ON PAGES 6–7.              │
└──────────────────────────────────────────────┘
```

Student Name _____

USE THIS PREWRITING PAGE TO
PLAN YOUR COMPOSITION.

MAKE SURE THAT YOU WRITE YOUR COMPOSITION ON
THE LINES ON PAGES 6–7.

Page 4

USE THIS PREWRITING PAGE TO
PLAN YOUR COMPOSITION.

MAKE SURE THAT YOU WRITE YOUR COMPOSITION
ON THE LINES ON PAGES 6–7.

Answer Document

_____

_____

_____

_____

_____

_____

_____

_____

_____

_____

_____

_____

_____

© Macmillan/McGraw-Hill

Page 6

Student Name _____

Answer Document

_____

_____

_____

_____

_____

_____

_____

_____

_____

_____

_____

_____

_____

_____

Page 7

STUDENT ANSWER SHEET

READING

1 (A) (B) (C) (D)	15 (A) (B) (C) (D)	29 (A) (B) (C) (D)
2 (F) (G) (H) (J)	16 (F) (G) (H) (J)	30 (F) (G) (H) (J)
3 (A) (B) (C) (D)	17 (A) (B) (C) (D)	31 (A) (B) (C) (D)
4 (F) (G) (H) (J)	18 (F) (G) (H) (J)	32 (F) (G) (H) (J)
5 (A) (B) (C) (D)	19 (A) (B) (C) (D)	33 (A) (B) (C) (D)
6 (F) (G) (H) (J)	20 (F) (G) (H) (J)	34 (F) (G) (H) (J)
7 (A) (B) (C) (D)	21 (A) (B) (C) (D)	35 (A) (B) (C) (D)
8 (F) (G) (H) (J)	22 (F) (G) (H) (J)	36 (F) (G) (H) (J)
9 (A) (B) (C) (D)	23 (A) (B) (C) (D)	37 (A) (B) (C) (D)
10 (F) (G) (H) (J)	24 (F) (G) (H) (J)	38 (F) (G) (H) (J)
11 (A) (B) (C) (D)	25 (A) (B) (C) (D)	39 (A) (B) (C) (D)
12 (F) (G) (H) (J)	26 (F) (G) (H) (J)	40 (F) (G) (H) (J)
13 (A) (B) (C) (D)	27 (A) (B) (C) (D)	41 (A) (B) (C) (D)
14 (F) (G) (H) (J)	28 (F) (G) (H) (J)	42 (F) (G) (H) (J)

STOP

STUDENT ANSWER SHEET

REVISING AND EDITING

S-1 Ⓐ Ⓑ Ⓒ Ⓓ   S-2 Ⓕ Ⓖ Ⓗ Ⓙ

1 Ⓐ Ⓑ Ⓒ Ⓓ	12 Ⓕ Ⓖ Ⓗ Ⓙ	23 Ⓐ Ⓑ Ⓒ Ⓓ
2 Ⓕ Ⓖ Ⓗ Ⓙ	13 Ⓐ Ⓑ Ⓒ Ⓓ	24 Ⓕ Ⓖ Ⓗ Ⓙ
3 Ⓐ Ⓑ Ⓒ Ⓓ	14 Ⓕ Ⓖ Ⓗ Ⓙ	25 Ⓐ Ⓑ Ⓒ Ⓓ
4 Ⓕ Ⓖ Ⓗ Ⓙ	15 Ⓐ Ⓑ Ⓒ Ⓓ	26 Ⓕ Ⓖ Ⓗ Ⓙ
5 Ⓐ Ⓑ Ⓒ Ⓓ	16 Ⓕ Ⓖ Ⓗ Ⓙ	27 Ⓐ Ⓑ Ⓒ Ⓓ
6 Ⓕ Ⓖ Ⓗ Ⓙ	17 Ⓐ Ⓑ Ⓒ Ⓓ	28 Ⓕ Ⓖ Ⓗ Ⓙ
7 Ⓐ Ⓑ Ⓒ Ⓓ	18 Ⓕ Ⓖ Ⓗ Ⓙ	29 Ⓐ Ⓑ Ⓒ Ⓓ
8 Ⓕ Ⓖ Ⓗ Ⓙ	19 Ⓐ Ⓑ Ⓒ Ⓓ	30 Ⓕ Ⓖ Ⓗ Ⓙ
9 Ⓐ Ⓑ Ⓒ Ⓓ	20 Ⓕ Ⓖ Ⓗ Ⓙ	31 Ⓐ Ⓑ Ⓒ Ⓓ
10 Ⓕ Ⓖ Ⓗ Ⓙ	21 Ⓐ Ⓑ Ⓒ Ⓓ	32 Ⓕ Ⓖ Ⓗ Ⓙ
11 Ⓐ Ⓑ Ⓒ Ⓓ	22 Ⓕ Ⓖ Ⓗ Ⓙ	

STOP

Form A Reading Answer Key

Question	Answer	Content Focus
1	D	Draw Conclusions
2	H	Author's Purpose
3	A	Summarize
4	G	Organizational Pattern
5	C	Dictionary
6	H	Sequence
7	D	Sequence
8	H	Information Presented Graphically
9	A	Roots and Affixes
10	F	Draw Conclusions
11	A	Synthesize/Make Connections
12	G	Synthesize/Make Connections
13	D	Synthesize/Make Connections
14	F	Synthesize/Make Connections
15	B	Context Clues/Multiple Meaning Words
16	G	Analogies
17	D	Author's Purpose
18	G	Summarize
19	D	Summarize
20	F	Fact and Opinion
21	C	Fact and Opinion

Question	Answer	Content Focus
22	H	Organizational Pattern
23	A	Organizational Pattern
24	F	Roots and Affixes
25	B	Analogies
26	J	Idioms
27	C	Context Clues
28	G	Sensory Language
29	C	Character
30	J	Narrative Point of View
31	A	Foreshadowing
32	H	Foreshadowing
33	B	Plot
34	H	Character
35	A	Multiple-Meaning Words
36	G	Dictionary
37	D	Dictionary
38	J	Structural Elements
39	B	Structural Elements
40	H	Sensory Language
41	B	Sensory Language
42	F	Sensory Language

Form A Revising and Editing Answer Key

Question	Answer	Content Focus
1	A	Revising and Editing
2	G	Punctuation
3	A	Spelling
4	H	Parts of Speech
5	B	Revising and Editing
6	H	Complete Sentences
7	A	Spelling
8	G	Complete Sentences
9	B	Complete Sentences
10	H	Spelling
11	B	Compound Sentences
12	F	Complete Sentences
13	B	Capitalization
14	F	Revising and Editing
15	C	Parts of Speech
16	G	Parts of Speech
17	B	Written Conventions
18	F	Compound Sentences
19	B	Parts of Speech
20	G	Parts of Speech
21	C	Parts of Speech
22	G	Compound Sentences
23	B	Spelling

Benchmark Assessment

Question	Answer	Content Focus
24	H	Revising and Editing
25	A	Capitalization
26	H	Parts of Speech
27	C	Revising and Editing
28	G	Compound Sentences
29	B	Punctuation
30	H	Spelling
31	C	Compound Sentences
32	F	Subject/Verb agreement

Form B Reading Answer Key

Question	Answer	Content Focus
1	C	Analogies
2	G	Roots and Affixes
3	C	Summarize
4	F	Draw Conclusions
5	D	Organizational Pattern
6	F	Author's Purpose
7	A	Multiple-Meaning Words
8	G	Text Features
9	C	Author's Viewpoint
10	J	Literary Nonfiction
11	D	Synthesize/Make Connections
12	F	Synthesize/Make Connections
13	B	Information Presented Graphically
14	F	Analogies
15	C	Idioms
16	H	Dictionary
17	C	Theme
18	F	Plot
19	C	Foreshadowing
20	H	Character
21	A	Narrative Point of View
22	G	Sensory Language
23	C	Dictionary

Benchmark Assessment

Question	Answer	Content Focus
24	G	Roots and Affixes
25	A	Context Clues
26	H	Author's Viewpoint
27	C	Persuasive Techniques
28	H	Information Presented Graphically
29	D	Interpret Details
30	G	Author's Purpose
31	A	Fact and Opinion
32	G	Organizational Pattern
33	C	Idioms
34	H	Context Clues
35	C	Theme
36	G	Plot
37	B	Foreshadowing
38	H	Foreshadowing
39	B	Plot
40	G	Character
41	C	Character
42	H	Theme

Form B Revising and Editing Answer Key

Question	Answer	Content Focus
1	C	Parts of Speech
2	H	Capitalization
3	A	Subject/Verb Agreement
4	J	Complete Sentences
5	C	Punctuation
6	H	Compound Sentences
7	B	Revising and Editing
8	G	Spelling
9	B	Parts of Speech
10	G	Punctuation
11	B	Revising and Editing
12	F	Spelling
13	D	Compound Sentences
14	G	Parts of Speech
15	A	Spelling
16	J	Compound Sentences
17	D	Parts of Speech
18	F	Spelling
19	A	Revising and Editing
20	J	Compound Sentences
21	B	Parts of Speech
22	G	Complete Sentences
23	A	Capitalization

Benchmark Assessment

Question	Answer	Content Focus
24	H	Revising and Editing
25	C	Parts of Speech
26	G	Subject/Verb Agreement
27	A	Spelling
28	F	Compound Sentences
29	C	Complete Sentences
30	G	Punctuation
31	A	Revising and Editing
32	H	Parts of Speech

WRITING RUBRICS
SCORE POINT 1

EACH COMPOSITION AT THIS SCORE POINT IS AN INEFFECTIVE PRESENTATION OF THE WRITER'S IDEAS.

Focus and Coherence

- Individual paragraphs and/or the entire composition are not focused. The writer may shift abruptly from idea to idea, making it difficult for the reader to understand how the ideas in the composition are related.

- The entire composition has little sense of completeness. The introduction and conclusion, if present, may be perfunctory.

- A large amount of writing may be unrelated and may not contribute to the development or quality of the entire composition. At times, the composition may be only weakly connected to the prompt.

Organization

- The writer's progression of thought between sentences and/or paragraphs is not logical. Occasionally weak progression results from a lack of transitions or from the use of transitions that do not make sense. At other times, the progression of thought is not evident, even if appropriate transitions are present.

- An organizational strategy is not evident. The writer may present ideas randomly, making the composition difficult to follow.

- Wordiness and/or repetition may inhibit the progression of ideas.

Development of Ideas

- The writer presents one or more ideas but provides little development of those ideas.

- The writer presents one or more ideas and makes an attempt to develop them. However, the development is general or vague, making it difficult for the reader to understand the writer's ideas.

- The writer presents only a plot summary of a published piece of writing, movie, or television show.

- The writer leaves out important information, which creates gaps between ideas. These gaps inhibit the reader's understanding of the ideas.

Voice

- The writer does not use language that engages the reader, and therefore fails to establish a connection.

- There may be no evidence of the writer's individual voice. The composition does not sound authentic or original. The writer does not express his/her individuality or unique perspective.

Conventions

- There is little evidence in the composition that the writer can correctly apply the English language conventions. Severe and/or frequent errors in spelling, capitalization, punctuation, grammar, usage, and sentence structure may cause the writing to be difficult to read. These errors weaken the composition by causing a lack of fluency.

- The writer may misuse or omit words and phrases, and may frequently include awkward sentences. These weaknesses inhibit the effective communication of ideas.

SCORE POINT 2

EACH COMPOSITION AT THIS SCORE POINT IS A SOMEWHAT EFFECTIVE PRESENTATION OF THE WRITER'S IDEAS.

Focus and Coherence
- Individual paragraphs and/or the entire composition are somewhat focused. The writer may shift quickly from idea to idea, but the reader can easily understand how the ideas in the composition are related.
- The entire composition has some sense of completeness. The writer includes an introduction and conclusion, but they may be superficial.
- Some of the writing may be unrelated and may not contribute to the development or quality of the entire composition.

Organization
- The writer's progression of thought between sentences and/or paragraphs may not always be smooth or logical. Occasionally, the writer should strengthen the progression by including more meaningful transitions; at other times the writer needs to establish stronger links between ideas.
- The organizational strategies the writer chooses do not allow the writer to present ideas effectively.
- Some wordiness and/or repetition may be present, but these weaknesses do not completely inhibit the progression of ideas.

Development of Ideas
- The writer attempts to develop the composition by listing or briefly explaining the ideas. The development remains superficial, preventing the reader's full understanding of the writer's ideas.
- The writer presents one or more ideas and attempts to develop them. There is little evidence of depth of thinking. The development may be mostly general, inconsistent, or contrived.
- The writer may leave out small pieces of information that create minor gaps between ideas. These gaps do not inhibit the reader's understanding of the ideas.

Voice
- There may be moments when the writer uses language that engages the reader, but the writer fails to sustain the connection.
- Individual paragraphs or sections of the composition sound authentic or original, but the writer does not generally express his/her individuality or unique perspective.

Conventions
- Errors in spelling, capitalization, punctuation, grammar, usage, and sentence structure throughout the composition may indicate a limited control of English language conventions. These errors may not cause the writing to be unclear, however they may weaken the overall fluency of the composition.
- The writer may employ simple or inaccurate words and phrases, and may write some awkward sentences. These weaknesses inhibit the overall effectiveness of the communication of ideas.

SCORE POINT 3

EACH COMPOSITION AT THIS SCORE POINT IS A GENERALLY EFFECTIVE PRESENTATION OF THE WRITER'S IDEAS.

Focus and Coherence

- Individual paragraphs and the composition are, for the most part, focused. The writer generally shows the distinct relationship between ideas, rarely making sudden shifts from one idea to the next.
- The composition has a sense of completeness. The introduction and conclusion add depth to the composition.
- Most of the writing contributes to the development or quality of the entire composition.

Organization

- The writer's progression of thought between sentences and/or paragraphs is, for the most part, smooth and controlled. Usually, transitions are meaningful, and the links between ideas are logical.
- The organizational strategies the writer chooses are usually effective.
- Wordiness and repetition, if present, are minor problems that do not inhibit the progression of ideas.

Development of Ideas

- The writer attempts to develop all the ideas in the composition. Some ideas may be developed more thoroughly and specifically than others, but the development reflects some depth of thought, allowing the reader to generally understand and appreciate the writer's ideas.
- The writer's presentation of some ideas may be thoughtful. Little evidence exists that the writer has been willing to take compositional risks when developing the topic.

Voice

- The writer uses language that engages the reader and sustains that connection throughout most of the composition.
- In general, the composition sounds authentic and original. The writer usually expresses his/her individuality or unique perspective.

Conventions

- There is evidence that the writer generally demonstrates a good command of spelling, capitalization, punctuation, grammar, usage, and sentence structure. Although there may be minor errors, they create few disruptions in the fluency of the composition.
- The words, phrases, and sentence structures the writer employs are generally appropriate and contribute to the overall effectiveness of the communication of ideas.

SCORE POINT 4

EACH COMPOSITION AT THIS SCORE POINT IS A HIGHLY EFFECTIVE PRESENTATION OF THE WRITER'S IDEAS.

Focus and Coherence

- Individual paragraphs and the entire composition are focused. This sustained focus allows the reader to understand how the ideas included in the composition are related.

- The entire composition has a sense of completeness. The introduction and conclusion add meaningful depth to the composition.

- Most, if not all, of the writing contributes to the development or quality of the entire composition.

Organization

- The writer's progression of thought between sentences and/or paragraphs is smooth and controlled. The writer's use of meaningful transitions and the logical movement from idea to idea strengthen this progression.

- The organizational strategies the writer chooses allow the writer to present ideas clearly and effectively.

Development of Ideas

- The writer's thorough and specific development of each idea creates depth of thought in the composition, allowing the reader to fully understand and appreciate the writer's ideas.

- The writer's presentation of ideas is thoughtful or insightful. The writer may approach the topic from an unusual perspective, use his/her unique experiences or view of the world as a basis for writing, or make interesting connections between ideas. In all these cases, the writer's willingness to take compositional risks improves the quality of the composition.

Voice

- The writer uses language that engages the reader and sustains this connection throughout the composition.

- The composition sounds authentic and original. The writer expresses his/her individuality or unique perspective.

Conventions

- The strength of the conventions contributes to the effectiveness of the composition. The writer demonstrates a consistent command of spelling, capitalization, punctuation, grammar, usage, and sentence structure. When the writer communicates complex ideas through advanced forms of expression, he/she may make minor errors as a result of these compositional risks. These types of errors do not take away from the overall fluency of the composition.

- The words, phrases, and sentence structures the writer uses enhance the effectiveness of the communication of ideas.

Anchor Papers: Student Writing Samples

This section provides sample written responses to the Benchmark Assessment writing prompts, along with comments explaining the scores.

Form A
SCORE POINT 1

I Like Baseball

I like to play baseball. Its fun and you get to play outside. Its good to play sports to be hellthy. Everyone shuld play sports cauz its fun and good exercise.

My team won the champinship this year. We had the best team ever and our couch said so. When you practice baseball you get good exercise too. I played first base and was a good hitter.

It is fun to watch baseball on TV. My favrite team is the Red Sox. They are awesome. It is an exciting game to watch. Especlly when the score is close.

Baseball is fun and hellthy too.

Focus and Coherence—composition has little sense of completeness and is not focused; writer shifts abruptly from winning the championship to watching baseball on television; difficult to understand how the ideas in the composition are related.

Organization—writer's progression of thought is not logical; lack of transitions throughout; ideas are presented randomly.

Development of Ideas—writer presents several ideas, including being on a team, watching baseball, and baseball as exercise but provides little development of ideas.

Voice—little evidence of the writer's individual voice; composition does not sound authentic or original.

Conventions—little evidence in the composition that the writer can correctly apply the English language conventions; many errors in spelling, punctuation, grammar, usage, and sentence structure; errors make writing difficult to read.

Benchmark Assessment

SCORE POINT 2

Why I Love Soccer

It is good for people to have a hobby, sport or other activity that they enjoy. Many people like to play sports. I like to play soccer. There are many reason why I like soccer.

Soccer is good exercize and that is good for you. I also like being outside when the weather is nice. You also learn the rules of the game you are playing and that is something good to know. Its good to be on a team. I learn to be a good teammate. Also I am a good goalie. I play goalie in hockey.

Today, kids spend so much time at school and they have a lot of home work to do. It is important to also have fun things to do.

Playing soccer is important because it is exciting it keeps you fit and most of all it is fun.

Focus and Coherence—composition is somewhat focused and has sense of completeness; writer shifts quickly from idea to idea, but the reader can understand how most of ideas are related; some unrelated information, such as the information about hockey.

Organization—writer's progression of thought is not always smooth; writer needs to include more meaningful transitions.

Development of Ideas—development remains superficial preventing the reader's full understanding of the writer's ideas; writer doesn't fully explain why it's good to be on a team; there is little evidence of depth of thinking.

Voice—writer uses some language that engages the reader but fails to sustain the connection.

Conventions—errors in spelling, capitalization, punctuation, grammar, usage, and sentence structure throughout the composition show a limited control of conventions; writer overuses words, such as "good," and includes awkward sentences.

SCORE POINT 3

It's Good to Have a Sport or Hobby

Most people know that playing a sport or having a hobby is good for them. The most important reason it is good to have a hobby or play a sport is because it is entertaining. Everyone needs a break after a hard day at work or school. A hobby or sport gives you that break.

Also, sports are a good physical activity. Your body needs to get a workout to keep it healthy. Playing a sport can keep you in good shape and help you stay healthy.

Having a hobby you find interesting, like making model planes, also can make you feel happy. When you feel like you are doing something special that you really enjoy its makes you happy.

Therefore, I think it is important for people to have a sport or hobby that they enjoy. It can help you relax, it can be good for your health, and it is something that is fun to do

Focus and Coherence—composition is for, the most part, focused and seems complete; writer shows relationship between ideas; most of the writing contributes to the development of the composition; conclusion summarizes composition's main points.

Organization—writer's progression of thought is smooth and controlled; transitions are meaningful, such as "therefore" in last paragraph; links between ideas are logical; no wordiness or repetition.

Development of Ideas—writer attempts to develop all the ideas in the composition; each paragraph develops an idea.

Voice—writer uses language that engages the reader and sustains that connection throughout most of the composition; composition sounds authentic and original.

Conventions—writer generally demonstrates a good command of spelling, capitalization, punctuation, grammar, usage, and sentence structure; words, phrases, and sentence structures are appropriate and contribute to the overall effectiveness of the communication of ideas.

SCORE POINT 4

Why a Sport or Hobby Is Important

It is very important for people to have a sport or hobby that they enjoy doing. These activities give people a break from their regular lives. They get to do something that they think is fun and maybe even exciting. Sports and hobbies can make people better rounded because they have two different parts of their lives—work and play.

In addition, sports is a good way to get exercise. Scientists are always telling us that we are getting too fat. Playing a sport is one way to help with this problem and keep people healthy.

People enjoy many different hobbies. Having a hobby gives people a chance to explore something that really interests them. In that way, they are giving their brain a workout. This keeps people healthy too.

Sports and hobbies give people a chance to feel good about what they are doing. This can help them feel good about themselves. Sports and hobbies can become a very special part of a person's life.

In conclusion, sports and hobbies are an important part of people's lives. They give you a chance to have fun, get good exercise, and learn interesting things.

Focus and Coherence—composition is focused and complete; introduction and conclusion add depth to the composition; most of the writing contributes to the development of the entire composition.

Organization—writer's progression of thought between sentences is smooth and controlled; writer uses meaningful transitions, such as "In addition," and "In conclusion"; organizational strategies allow the writer to present ideas clearly and effectively.

Development of Ideas—writer's thorough and specific development of each idea creates depth of thought in the composition, allowing the reader to fully understand and appreciate the writer's ideas.

Voice—writer uses language that engages the reader and sustains this connection throughout the composition; composition sounds authentic and original.

Conventions—writer demonstrates a consistent command of spelling, capitalization, punctuation, grammar, usage, and sentence structure; words, phrases, and sentence structures the writer uses enhance the effectiveness of the communication of ideas.

No School for Summer

I dont want to go to school in the summer. It will be stupid to go to school all year.

I want to play outside in the summer. I go to my granma's house evry summer and play with my cuzins. I don't want to miss it ever. We go to play in the park and have good times together. My granma live by a lake. Also we go to the lake and swim for hours. I am a fast swimer. And I take lesons.

Summer is my favrite time of year. I dont want to miss summer.

Focus and Coherence—composition has little sense of completeness; there is not a developed introduction or conclusion; much of the writing is unrelated; composition is only weakly connected to the prompt.

Organization—writer's progression of thought is not logical; lack of transitions throughout; organizational strategy is not evident; writer presents ideas randomly, making the composition difficult to follow.

Development of Ideas—writer makes some attempt to develop idea in main paragraph, however, the development is very general and difficult for the reader to understand.

Voice—writer does not use language that engages the reader; no evidence of the writer's individual voice.

Conventions—frequent errors in spelling, capitalization, punctuation, grammar, usage, and sentence structure make the writing to difficult to read.

© Macmillan/McGraw-Hill

SCORE POINT 2

Should We Go to School All Year?

I think that going to school all year long is a good idea. I think that the school year should be changed to include the summer.

We would gets smarter if we go to school in the summer. We would be able to take more time to learn hard subjects. That would really help me out. I would get better in math. We could get ahead of other kids who get the summer off. Other contryes have school for much longer then us. It is easier for them to learn hard subjects.

A lot of people probly won't agree with me. But I think it is important to do good in school. That is why I think everyone should go to school in the summer.

Focus and Coherence—composition is somewhat focused; writer shifts quickly from idea to idea, but the reader can easily understand how the ideas in the composition are related; composition has some sense of completeness.

Organization—progression of thought is not always smooth; writer should strengthen the progression by including more meaningful transitions; some repetition of ideas is present.

Development of Ideas—writer attempts to develop the composition but development remains superficial, such as the mention of other countries having longer school years.

Voice—writer is sometimes able to engage the reader but fails to sustain the connection; writer does not generally express his/her individuality or unique perspective.

Conventions—errors in spelling, capitalization, punctuation, grammar, and usage throughout; errors weaken the overall fluency of the composition; writer uses simple words and phrases and some awkward sentences.

SCORE POINT 3

Not In Favor of School in the Summer

I think that extending the school year to include the summer months is a terrible idea. Children need a break from all the hard work they do during the year. I believe in this saying: "All work and no play make Johnny a dull boy."

Obviously, we all feel that a good education is important. However, children are more than their brains. They need to go outside and have fun. That is what the summertime is all about.

After some time away from school, we feel refreshed and ready to go back and learn some more. If we go to school all through the hot summer months, we will never get a chance to rest and recharge our batteries.

For these reasons, I believe that it is a bad idea to extend the school year to include the summer months. It is important for children to have some time for fun.

Focus and Coherence—individual paragraphs and the composition are, for the most part, focused; writer shows relationship between ideas; composition has a sense of completeness; no extraneous information.

Organization—writer's progression of thought is smooth and controlled; transitions are meaningful and the links between ideas are logical; composition is well-organized.

Development of Ideas—writer attempts to develop all the ideas in the composition; some ideas developed more thoroughly and specifically than others, the development reflects some depth of thought, readers can understand and appreciate the writer's ideas.

Voice—writer uses language that engages the reader and sustains that connection throughout most of the composition; use of quote in the first paragraph is engaging; composition sounds authentic and original.

Conventions—writer demonstrates a good command of spelling, capitalization, punctuation, grammar, usage, and sentence structure.

SCORE POINT 4

School All Year: A Good Decision

Generations of students have looked forward to summer vacation every year. However, today there are many people who think that the school year should last all year. I feel that this is a very good idea. Here are some reasons why.

First, the most important thing we can do is get an education. The early years are when our brain can take in the most information.

Second, I don't feel that ten months is enough time to get a good education. With a longer school year, we can spend more time on interesting subjects and learn more things.

Finally, a good education is a key to the future. Without a good education, you probably won't get a decent job and your future might be bleak. If we extend the school year, we will get a much better education and a much brighter future.

For these reasons, I strongly believe that extending the schoolyear is the best thing to do for a good education.

Focus and Coherence—individual paragraphs and the entire composition are focused; composition has a sense of completeness; introduction and conclusion add depth.

Organization—composition is well-organized and writer's progression of thought is smooth; meaningful transitions, such as "First," "Second," and "Finally," strengthen progression of ideas.

Development of Ideas—writer fully develops each idea; reader can understand and appreciate the writer's ideas; writer's presentation of ideas is thoughtful.

Voice—writer uses engaging language; composition sounds authentic and original; writer expresses unique perspective.

Conventions—writer demonstrates a consistent command of spelling, capitalization, punctuation, grammar, and usage.

Teacher Notes

Teacher Notes

Teacher Notes

Teacher Notes